CONTENTS

Chapter One: Cancer Prevalence

What is cancer?	1
What causes cancer?	2
Ten questions about breast problems	3
You don't have to be female to get breast cancer	5
Global cancer cases 'to soar to 20 million'	7
Women risk most deadly lung cancer	8
The passive killer	9
Passive smoke row	10
The sun and your skin	11
Skin cancer	12
Cervical cancer research	13
Cervical cancer deaths fall by 40 per cent	14
Cervical screening	15
The cancer young men ignore at their peril	16
Testicular cancer	18
Prostate cancer	20
Why don't we all get cancer?	22
Close relationships and cancer	23
Mobile phones 'could be to blame for cancer surge'	25

Chapter Two: Treatment and Cures

More beat cancer, but UK trails other countries for cures	26
Surviving cancer	26
The cancer lottery	27
Good screen guide	28
The essential guide to breast awareness	29
The deadly delays	32
Sun protection and sunscreens	33
Childhood cancer	34
Right diet may help prevent cancer	35
Cancer: the high-risk diets and lifestyles	35
New approaches to cancer	36
Cancer and complementary therapies	38
A risk worth taking?	39
Cancer vaccine may end chemotherapy	40
Additional resources	41
Index	42
Web site information	43
Acknowledgements	44

Introduction

Cancer is the forty-second volume in the series: **Issues**. The aim of this series is to offer up-to-date information about important issues in our world.

Cancer looks at the causes and types of cancer, cancer treatments and the search for cures.

The information comes from a wide variety of sources and includes:
Government reports and statistics
Newspaper reports and features
Magazine articles and surveys
Literature from lobby groups
and charitable organisations.

It is hoped that, as you read about the many aspects of the issues explored in this book, you will critically evaluate the information presented. It is important that you decide whether you are being presented with facts or opinions. Does the writer give a biased or an unbiased report? If an opinion is being expressed, do you agree with the writer?

Cancer offers a useful starting-point for those who need convenient access to information about the many issues involved. However, it is only a starting-point. At the back of the book is a list of organisations which you may want to contact for further information.

*****

Cancer

ISSUES
(formerly Issues for the Nineties)

Volume 42

Editor

Craig Donnellan

Independence
Educational Publishers
Cambridge

First published by Independence
PO Box 295
Cambridge CB1 3XP
England

British Library Cataloguing in Publication Data
Cancer – (Issues Series)
I. Donnellan, Craig II. Series
616.9'94

ISBN 1 86168 094 5

Printed in Great Britain
The Burlington Press
Cambridge

Typeset by
Claire Boyd

Cover
The illustration on the front cover is by
Pumpkin House.

CHAPTER ONE: CANCER PREVALENCE

What is cancer?

Information from the CRC Institute for Cancer Studies at the University of Birmingham

Your body is made up of billions of cells that can only be seen under a microscope. These cells are grouped together to make up the tissues and organs of our bodies. They are a bit like building blocks.

Genes and cancer

There are many different types of cells in the body which do different jobs, but they are basically similar. They all have a centre called a nucleus. Inside the nucleus are the genes. Genes are really bits of code. The information they carry can be switched on or off. The genes control the cell. They decide when it will reproduce, what it does and even when it will die.

Normally the genes make sure that cells grow and reproduce in an orderly and controlled way. If the system goes wrong for any reason, the usual result is that the cell dies. Rarely, the system goes wrong in a way that allows a cell to keep on dividing until a lump called a 'tumour' is formed.

Benign and malignant tumours

Tumours (lumps) can be benign or malignant. Benign means not cancer. Benign tumours:
- Usually grow quite slowly.
- Do not spread to other parts of the body.
- Usually have a covering that is made up of normal cells.

Benign tumours are made up of cells that are quite similar to normal cells. They will only cause a problem if they:

- Grow very large.
- Become uncomfortable or unsightly.
- Press on other body organs.
- Are taking up space inside the skull.
- Release hormones that affect how the body functions.

Malignant tumours are made up of cancer cells. They:
- Usually grow faster than benign tumours.
- Spread through and destroy surrounding tissues.
- Spread to other parts of the body.

It is the ability to spread that makes a cancer dangerous. If a cancer is not treated, it can threaten the organs near to where it started growing. It can also damage other parts of the body by spreading.

Primary and secondary cancer

The place where a cancer begins is called the 'primary cancer'. But the cancer cells can spread. They can break away and are carried in the blood or lymphatic system to other parts of the body. There they can start to grow new tumours. These are the 'secondary cancers'. Doctors sometimes call these metastases and say a cancer that has spread has 'metastasised'.

The various organs of the body are made up of different types of cells. Any of these cell types can grow into a primary cancer. Cancers from different cell types behave differently. They can:
- Grow at different speeds.
- Have various effects on the body. by releasing chemicals into the blood.
- Be more or less likely to spread in the blood.
- Respond differently to drugs.
- Respond differently to radiation.

Cancers can cause different symptoms in different people because of where they are. A cancer may press on a nerve, or another body organ that is nearby. The place where the cancer starts also affects what treatment can be used because doctors have to take into account the risk of damaging neighbouring organs.

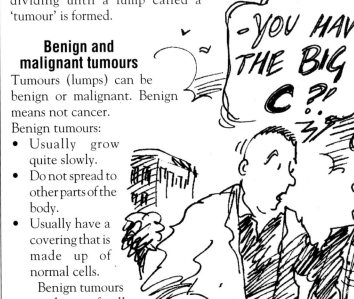

- The above is an extract from the CRC Institute for Cancer Studies at the University of Birmingham web site which can be found at http://medweb.bham.ac.uk/cancer help/

What causes cancer?

Information from the CRC Institute for Cancer Studies at the University of Birmingham

What causes cancer?

This is not as simple a question as it sounds because:

- There are many different types of cancer.
- More than one 'cause' is often involved.

There are about 200 different types of cancer affecting the different body tissues. What affects one body tissue may not affect another. For example, tobacco smoke that you breathe in may help to cause lung cancer. Overexposing your skin to the sun could give you a melanoma on your leg. But the sun won't give you lung cancer and smoking won't give you melanoma.

Apart from infectious diseases, most illnesses are 'multi-factorial'. And cancer is no exception. Multi-factorial means that there are many factors involved. In other words, there is no single cause for any one cancer. These are some of the factors involved in getting a cancer:

- Age
- Your genetic make-up
- Your immune system
- Your diet
- Your day-to-day environment
- Viruses

A 'carcinogen' is something that can help to cause cancer. Tobacco smoke is a powerful carcinogen. But not everyone who smokes gets lung cancer. So there must be other factors at work.

Age

Most types of cancer become more common as we get older. This is because the changes that cause a cell to become cancerous in the first place take a long time to develop. There have to be a number of changes to the genes within a cell before it turns into a cancer cell. The changes can happen by accident when the cell is dividing.

Or they can happen because the cell has been damaged by carcinogens and the damage is then passed on to future 'daughter' cells when that cell divides. The longer we live, the more time there is for us to accumulate these genetic mistakes in our cells.

Genetic make-up

There have to be a number of genetic mutations within a cell before it becomes cancerous. Sometimes we are born with one of these mutations already. This does not mean we will get cancer. But with one mutation from the outset, it makes it more likely statistically that we will. Doctors call this 'genetic pre-disposition'.

The BRCA1 breast cancer gene is an example of genetic pre-disposition. Women who carry this faulty gene have a higher chance of developing breast cancer than women who do not.

BRCA1 is a good example for another reason. Most women with breast cancer do not have the mutated BRCA1 gene. Only about 5% of all breast cancer is due to this gene. So although women with this gene are individually more likely to get breast cancer, most breast cancer is not caused by an inherited faulty gene.

This is true of other common cancers where some people have a genetic predisposition, for example colon (large bowel) cancer.

The immune system

People who have problems with their immune systems are more likely to get some forms of cancer. This group includes people who:

- Have had organ transplants and take drugs to suppress their immune systems to stop organ rejection.
- Have AIDS.
- Are born with rare medical syndromes which affect their immunity.

The kinds of extra cancers that affect these groups of people fall into two, overlapping groups:

- Cancers that are caused by viruses, such as cervical cancer or some lymphomas.
- Lymphomas.

Chronic infections or trans-planted organs can continually stimulate cells to divide. This continual cell division means that

immune cells are more likely to acquire mutations and develop into lymphomas.

Diet

Cancer experts estimate that changes to our diet could prevent about one in three cancer deaths in the UK. In the western world, many of us eat too many animal fats and not enough fresh fruit and vegetables. This type of diet is known to increase your risk of cancer. But how exactly we should alter our diets is not clear.

Sometimes foods or food additives are blamed for directly causing cancer and described as 'carcinogenic'. This is often a distortion of the truth. Sometimes a food is found to contain a substance that can cause cancer but in such small amounts that we could never eat enough of it to do any harm. And some additives may actually protect us.

Day-to-day environment

By this we mean what is around you each day that may help to cause cancer. This could include:
- Tobacco smoke
- The sun
- Natural and man-made radiation
- Workplace hazards
- Asbestos

Some of these are avoidable and some aren't. Most are only contributing factors to causing cancers – part of the jigsaw puzzle that scientists are still trying to put together.

Viruses

Viruses can help to cause some cancers. But this does not mean that these cancers can be caught like an infection. What happens is that the virus can cause genetic changes in cells that make them more likely to become cancerous.

These cancers and viruses are linked:
- Cervical cancer and the genital wart virus, HPV.
- Primary liver cancer and the Hepatitis B virus.
- T cell leukaemia in adults and the Human T cell leukaemia virus.

Not all the people with these cancers will have been infected with the related virus. But infection may increase their risk of getting that particular cancer.

Many people can be infected with a cancer-causing virus, and never get cancer. The virus only causes cancer in certain situations. An example is Epstein-Barr virus (EBV). These are some facts about this common virus:
- Most people are infected with EBV.
- People who catch it late get glandular fever but this does not cause cancer.
- In sub-Saharan Africa, EBV infection and repeated attacks of malaria together cause a cancer called Burkitt's lymphoma that affects children.
- In China, EBV infection (together with other unknown factors) causes naso-pharyngeal cancer.
- In AIDs patients and transplant patients EBV can cause lymphoma.
- In the UK, about 4 out of 10 cases of Hodgkin's disease seem to be related to EBV infection.

• The above is an extract from the CRC Institute for Cancer Studies at the University of Birmingham web site which can be found at http://medweb.bham.ac.uk/cancer help/

© CRC Institute for Cancer Studies at the University of Birmingham 1998

Ten questions about breast problems

Ten typical kinds of questions asked on the Women's Nationwide Cancer Control Campaign (WNCCC) HELPLINE regarding breast problems

Q1. I have found a lump in my breast. I am too frightened to see my GP. Could it be cancer? What will they do if I have to go to hospital?

It can be very frightening to discover a lump in your breast – and many women are afraid to go to their GP when they find a lump. Maybe you're thinking, 'Is it serious? If it is, then I'd rather not know. I'd rather not think about it at all!'

One comforting fact about breast lumps is that 9 out of 10 of them are found to be benign and harmless. Only 1 in 10 turn out to be cancer when all the tests have been done. Nevertheless, it is essential that you first go and see your GP. When you go to your GP, he/she will examine your breast. If it's not possible to say exactly what the lump is you'll be referred to the breast clinic at your local hospital for a thorough examination.

At the breast outpatient clinic you'll be examined by a specialist who will decide what investigations will be needed. The usual ones are mammography (breast x-ray), ultrasound and fine needle aspiration, which involves inserting a needle into the lump and drawing off fluid or a small sample of tissue which can be sent to the laboratory. It's a good idea to ask someone to go with you to the breast clinic to offer some support.

Before you attend the breast clinic, it's worth finding out how and when you'll get your results. Some clinics can give the results on the same day. Other will ask you to make another appointment to get your results. It depends on the local arrangements.

Q2. I have a lump in my breast. I saw my GP who said to come back after my period. Is that alright, or should I see someone else?
Some breast lumps are related to changes in the hormone levels. They may become smaller or even disappear entirely after your monthly period. If the lump disappears there is no need to worry any more. However, if you have a persistent breast lump you will need to be referred to a breast clinic.

Q3. What does 'breast awareness' mean and how do I check my breasts?
'Breast awareness' is about getting to know your breasts and finding what is normal for you. When you know how your breasts normally look and feel, then it will be easy to notice any changes. It is really a good idea to get to know your breasts at different times in your monthly cycle. Many women find that they have lumpy breasts which become tender, or even painful, before their period begins. Once the period is over, the tenderness usually disappears and the breasts feel softer and less lumpy.

It is essential that you feel your breasts with the flat of the fingers. Otherwise you will find all the lumps and bumps that are simply part of the normal breast tissue. Some women prefer feeling their breasts with a soapy hand when they're in the bath or shower. Others prefer to check their breasts lying down.

Any change which is *new for you* needs to be checked by your GP or practice nurse. Most changes are not a sign of cancer. In fact, 9 out of 10 breast lumps are not cancer and are generally harmless. If a change does turn out to be due to cancer, then the earlier it is treated, the better. Early detection gives the best chance of simple and effective treatment.

Q4. I am very worried about getting breast cancer. What are the main risk factors?
There are various risk factors but by far the most significant is increasing

age – the older you get, the higher your risk of getting breast cancer. This is the main reason for offering breast screening to women over the age of 50. Having a higher risk of getting cancer does *not* mean that a women will automatically get the disease. Many women live to a ripe old age and are never troubled by breast cancer.

It is important to bear this in mind when thinking about other risk factors. Some of them are:
- having your first child after the age of 30
- never having children
- starting your periods at age 11, or younger
- having a late menopause.

There is also the question of 'family history'. A small number of women may be at higher risk because they inherited a faulty gene when they were born. This means that breast cancer may 'run in the family'. If you are worried about whether you may be at risk, talk to your GP.

Taking Hormone Replacement Therapy (HRT) may slightly increase your risk of developing breast cancer. This risk increases the longer HRT is taken. However, about five years after stopping HRT the risk is the same as if you had never taken HRT. It seems that women who take the contraceptive pill also have a slightly increased risk. This is also temporary and will disappear completely once a woman has been off the pill for 10

years. There has been much discussion about diet and its effect on the risk of getting breast cancer. The full picture is still unclear. General health advice suggests increasing your daily intake of vegetables and fresh fruit, limiting alcohol consumption and not smoking.

Men can also get breast cancer, but this is rare.

Q5. I have just been diagnosed with breast cancer and have no idea what's going to happen. Who can I talk to?
One person who you can talk to in detail is your consultant at the hospital. They have the specialist knowledge and the results of all the test that have been done – including details about the type of breast cancer thats you have. Another important source of support and information is the breast care nurse who works with your consultant. They can also explain anything you don't understand and talk over any decisions that you may have to make.

There are three helpful organisations which can provide information and other services for women with breast cancer. These are: Breast Cancer Care on 0500 245324, Cancerbacup on 0808 8001234 and Cancerlink on 0800 132905. They all provide support and a range of useful information.

Q6. My breasts are different sizes. Is this anything to worry about?
Most women's breasts are different sizes and if yours have always been like that, then you don't need to worry. However, if this is something new for you, then it's a good idea to see your GP for a (check up).

Q7. My mother had breast cancer when she was 46 and her sister at 39. I heard that breast cancer could run in families. What should I do?
In recent years, family cancer clinics have been set up throughout the UK in regional genetics centres to help people who have a 'significant family history'.

You would need to be referred by your GP and you would need to collect as much information about those members of your family who have had breast cancer and/or ovarian cancer – including their age when they were diagnosed. The doctor at the clinic will be able to advise you whether your own risk is higher then the average, and whether screening for breast cancer is a good idea. Even if you have a family history of breast cancer, it does not automatically mean you or other relatives will get the disease.

Q8. I have got a creamy discharge from my nipples. What could it be?
This discharge is probably not a sign of anything serious like cancer. However, if you have any sort of discharge from the nipples, see your GP.

Q9. I would like to have a mammogram. Can you tell me where I can get this done?
All women between the ages of 50 and 64 who are registered with a GP are invited for a mammogram every 3 years. The NHS Breast Screening Service sends out the invitations based on the GP's list. At the moment, if you are over 64 you are welcome to have free mammograms but you will have to make your own appointment. Ask your GP about this.

If there is something you are worried about, like a lump, then it's best to talk it over with your GP. Sometimes it's advisable to have other tests done alongside mammography to put your mind at rest.

Q10. I have had painful breasts for a few months now. My GP suggested evening primrose oil, but it hasn't made any difference. Is there anything else that can be done?
Evening primrose oil can take at least three months before it begins to have an effect. It's important to notice whether your pain changes at different times in your monthly cycle. Evening primrose oil is usually recommended for what is known as 'cyclical breast pain'. This kind of breast pain is usually worse just before a period and subsides when the period is over.

It can help to wear a well-fitting, supportive bra even in bed. Some women find it useful to have a bra properly fitted at the shop. Some health care professionals suggests that women with cyclical breast pain should cut down on caffeine in tea and coffee. Simple painkillers such as paracetamol can also help.
• We hope this has been of help and that it covers many of the questions you had. If you need any further information or publications, please contact the Women's Nationwide Cancer Control Campaign (WNCCC) on 0171 729 4688. Alternatively, if you have any questions and would like to speak to someone, you may wish to contact one of the following helplines: CancerBACUP on 0808 800 1234 or Cancerlink on 0800 132905.

You don't have to be female to get breast cancer

No breasts? You can still get breast cancer. And men who put off seeing a doctor about a lump are at high risk. By Roger Dobson

Stephen Wilshere was returning home from a summer holiday when he felt a lump on his right breast. He was certain it had not been there before, and prodded again to make sure it was real. 'It was a very hot Sunday, and I had put my hand under my shirt to scratch my shoulder when I felt this hard lump. I didn't say anything at the time . . . but the next day I showed my wife and she said I ought to see the doctor.'

A few days later, after a biopsy, he was diagnosed with breast cancer and within a fortnight the ex-pilot and retired computer specialist had a mastectomy, followed by radiotherapy and treatment with tamoxifen.

Breast cancer affects one in 1,000 men, compared to one in 11 women. But a new study suggests that men who are high achievers may carry a much greater than average risk of the disease. Researchers found that rates were highest among graduates, men on high incomes, and those with assets of £35,000-plus.

Breast cancer in men and women is essentially the same disease, so researchers believe that studying it in men may be an effective way of investigating environmental causes.

Breast cancer affects one in 1,000 men, compared to one in 11 women

---

Dr Ann Hsing and her team believe that the investigation of male breast cancer may provide unique clues about environmental and occupational risks that are difficult to detect in women. This is because they can be masked by confounding factors such as pregnancy, breastfeeding and age at menstruation.

Male breast cancer is much rarer, but one of the problems is men's reluctance to see a doctor. While messages aimed at women have been highly successful in raising awareness of the disease and promoting self-examination, men are still in the dark ages of health education.

'The worst aspect of male breast cancer is that men are dying of ignorance,' says Professor Ian Fentiman, professor of surgical oncology at Guy's Hospital. 'We are still finding that the average duration of symptoms is six to nine months.

'That's a long delay, and the reason is that men don't even think about it as a possibility. The real message is that if a man finds a lump on one side it needs to be looked at, particularly if it is not painful.'

Treatment for male breast cancer is similar to that for women, but usually involves a mastectomy because there is too little tissue for more conservative surgery to be effective. That is usually backed up by removal of the lymph glands, radiotherapy for the chest wall and treatment with tamoxifen, which appears to have good results with hormone-sensitive male breast cancers.

Men get breast cancer seven years later than women, on average, but survival rates are almost exactly the same for both sexes if they report their symptoms at the same stage. However, the overall outcome is worse for men because they tend to get diagnosed much later.

One of the mysteries surrounding male breast cancer is the cause, especially in men who do not carry a gene that predisposes for the disease. Over the years a range of culprits have been looked at, including high-temperature jobs that may affect the testes, and overhead power cables which have been thought to affect the release of the hormone melatonin from the pineal gland.

The environmental effects of exposure to hormones from the female contraceptive pill have been investigated; so, too, have various occupational carcinogens, cosmetics and perfumes.

'A whole range of things have been looked at. We are not sure, for example, whether electromagnetic fields are a risk factor. There was a study which suggested that people who worked with generators and transformers might have a slight increase in risk. The perfume industry has been looked at, and at one time the wearing of braces was considered, but that has been discredited,' says Prof Fentiman.

'I don't think there is any occupation where you can turn around and say, "this job is a serious

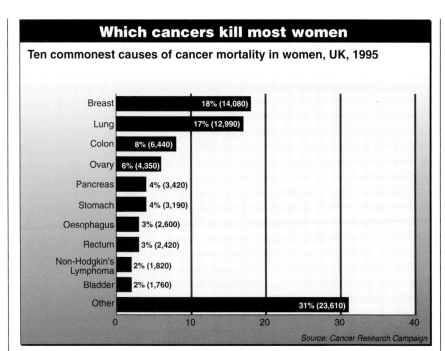

Which cancers kill most women

Ten commonest causes of cancer mortality in women, UK, 1995

Cancer	Percentage (number)
Breast	18% (14,080)
Lung	17% (12,990)
Colon	8% (6,440)
Ovary	6% (4,350)
Pancreas	4% (3,420)
Stomach	4% (3,190)
Oesophagus	3% (2,600)
Rectum	3% (2,420)
Non-Hodgkin's Lymphoma	2% (1,820)
Bladder	2% (1,760)
Other	31% (23,610)

Source: Cancer Research Campaign

risk factor for male breast cancer." The trouble is that you are dealing with small numbers, so there will always be the risk of chance associations.'

Research carried out by Dr Anne Hsing of the US National Cancer Institute and colleagues in Italy shows that although risk factors cannot be pinned down with any certainty to specific jobs, they can be linked to social class and wealth.

The research, reported in the *Journal of Occupational and Environmental Health*, examines the cases of 201 men who died from breast cancer and finds clear differences in socioeconomic circumstances. Those with family incomes above £35,000 had a 50 per cent greater risk than those on lower incomes. Men with assets greater than £35,000 were twice as likely to get the disease as those with few or no assets; those who went to college were also at twice as much risk as men who left school early.

Similar observations have been made by Professor Fentiman in his own practice in London: 'I have quite a lot of patients with male breast cancer who are high-flying executives,' he says.

Just what that means is not clear, but one lifestyle variable between socioeconomic groups is diet.

'As well as reproductive factors, other factors that are related to high socioeconomic status, such as diet and other lifestyle habits, may be important, and deserve further investigation,' says Dr Hsing.

For some men, like Stephen Wilshere, the matter is more clear-cut. He carries the gene for breast cancer that caused the death of his mother and one of his daughters. 'I have been tested to see whether I am carrying the gene for breast cancer, and I am. It means a one in two chance that any of my children will also carry the gene. If they are male and they are carrying it, there is a 10 per cent chance of their developing cancer, but for females it is between 80 and 85 per cent.'

Since his mastectomy, he has worked as a volunteer for Breast Cancer Care, helping other men to come to terms with their diagnosis. 'When they get the results, it affects different people in different ways. Some doctors are wonderful at breaking the news, and others are terrible; they back into the furthest corner of the room and say something like, "I don't think I've very good news for you",' he says.

The message for men, he concludes, is to get symptoms checked early and to remember that taking out the tumour is not the end of the story: 'Anyone can remove the lump; the clever thing is to stop the little bugger coming back again.'

• Breast Cancer Care's free help line deals with concern about male breast cancer: 0500 245345

© The Independent
September, 1998

Global cancer cases 'to soar to 20 million'

By Aisling Irwin,
Science Correspondent

Cancer will be the major global health problem within two decades, the World Health Organisation forecast yesterday.

By the year 2020, the number of cancer cases is expected to have soared from the current 10 million a year to 20 million. In Britain, it is predicted that one in two people will develop the disease, compared with the one in three today.

The warning came as the WHO began a world-wide programme of cancer control in London, marking a fundamental change in policy. The organisation's attention until now has been on infectious and parasitical diseases such as tuberculosis and malaria.

Professor Karol Sikora, chief of the WHO cancer programme, said that the epidemic of cancer was mainly the result of successful health strategies that had led to longer life expectancy and the population boom.

'The pattern has changed,' he said. 'The infectious diseases of the past are now, on the whole, cheaper to treat and we have been successful with vaccination and sanitation.'

Instead, people were living to 50 and developing cancer. In addition, the adoption of the Western lifestyle by developing countries had led to soaring levels of smoking and an unhealthy diet that would contribute about 10 per cent – or one million – of the rise in cancer cases.

The cost of looking after people with long-lasting chronic diseases would be huge, the London meeting heard.

'It is partly a good thing because it means that people are not dying of infection as children,' said Prof Sikora. 'But you have to treat cancer patients. Cancer is expensive. It causes prolonged suffering. These sufferers are not going to be old people, they are going to be 50 to 55-year-olds. The main result of this

will be a huge increase in human suffering and disability.'

Middle-income countries were expected to bear the brunt of the cancer epidemic, and more than half of the cancer victims would therefore live in countries that had between them less than five per cent of the world's cancer-treating resources.

Prof Sikora said: 'In the developing world 80 per cent of cancers are seen only at a late stage when there is not much that can be done. This compares with 20 per cent in the developed world.'

The meeting heard that a quarter of all cancers could be prevented by applying existing knowledge about the links between the disease and known causes such as smoking and a poor diet.

A third of people could be cured if they had access to current technology and it should be possible to cure half of cancers in 25 years' time.

The WHO's cancer control programme aimed to reduce the expected cancer toll by five million a year by the year 2020.

In another fundamental change for the WHO, part of its campaign was to attract the private sector into helping tackle cancer. It wanted to encourage health insurance companies and the drug and food industries to help set up new infrastructures and new health markets.

Prof Sikora said: 'We have a responsibility, as leaders in world health, to find and promote ways to reduce that coming burden.

'But this can't be achieved through governmental efforts alone, divorced from the resources and expertise that exists with the private sector.'

Sir Kenneth Calman, who recently retired as Britain's Chief Medical Officer and who chairs the WHO executive board, said: 'The way forward is through the development of national cancer programmes that establish priorities for development in each country.

'These will take into account both the types of cancer that are prevalent in a country and its economy.'

Women risk most deadly lung cancer

Female smokers are twice as likely as men to develop inoperable form of the disease. By Glenda Cooper, Social Affairs Correspondent

Women smokers are more likely than men to develop the most serious form of lung cancer, possibly because of the way they smoke cigarettes, according to new research.

The study by the British Thoracic Society (BTS) – the largest British investigation into lung cancer – found that nearly twice as many women as men under the age of 65 are diagnosed with small cell lung cancer, the most dangerous form of the disease.

Seven out of ten of these cases could not be helped by surgery and more than half will be dead within six months of their diagnosis.

The findings reinforced calls by the BTS, the UK's official body of respiratory specialists, for the Government to target teenage girls in its imminent White Paper on tobacco.

The study found that men were more likely to have non-small cell lung cancer, which is less damaging to the lung, and nearly half could be considered operable.

Dr Mike Pearson, chairman of the BTS Public Education Committee, said there were several reasons why women might be more susceptible to small cell lung cancer.

'Our research suggests women have less resistance to the most dangerous kinds of lung cancer,' he said. 'This may be due to changing patterns of smoking behaviour – many women took up the habit a decade after men, who smoked heavily during the Second World War.

'Women may also smoke in a different way to men, for example taking shorter, sharper inhalations, which could have an effect on the kind and severity of cancer that they develop.'

Action on Smoking and Health (ASH) claimed that the higher levels

SIMON KNEEBONE

of small cell lung cancer among female smokers could be explained by their tendency to take 'sharper inhalations' because they smoke 'lighter' cigarettes.

'There are probably several factors at work here, but a major suspect is the greater use of "light" cigarettes by women,' said Clive Bates, director of ASH. 'People adjust their smoking to get a satisfying dose of nicotine, and "low-tar" smokers draw smoke more deeply into the lungs to get the nicotine they need.'

Dr Pearson said: 'Smoking among teenage girls is on the increase. It is vitally important that young women know the greater risks they are running by smoking. We must prevent them becoming the lung cancer victims of the future.'

The Health Minister, Tessa Jowell, said yesterday that the Government wanted to tackle the increasing rate of smoking among teenage girls. 'Ten years ago, one in five 15-year-old girls smoked. That figure is now one in three,' she said. 'Smoking is the single greatest cause of preventable death and there is no safe level at which people can smoke.'

Dr Pearson urged the Government to act more quickly to ban tobacco advertising and sponsorship amid signs it could take years for the ban to be implemented. 'If you stop smoking, you halve your risk in five years. Waiting seven years, in our view, is longer than is necessary,' he said. 'It's vital young women know the greater risks they're running by smoking.'

© The Independent
December, 1998

The passive killer

Other people's cigarette smoke does cause cancer, scientists confirm

Scientists are calling for drastic curbs on smoking in public places after a report concluded that passive smoking does cause lung cancer.

The report from the Government-backed Scientific Committee on Tobacco and Health rejects claims by the tobacco industry at the weekend that no link could be proved between passive smoking and lung cancer.

As well as lung cancer, passive smoking can also cause heart disease and poses a special threat to babies and children, it says.

Babies whose parents smoke are twice as likely to be victims of sudden infant death and have a 50 per cent increased risk of suffering serious breathing difficulties. Asthma attacks, bronchitis, pneumonia and glue ear can all be triggered.

People who regularly breathe in others' smoke have an increased risk of lung cancer and heart disease.

Those living with a smoker have a 20 to 30 per cent increased risk of lung cancer and a 23 per cent increased risk of heart disease.

As for smokers themselves, half are killed by the habit unless they quit, the report says.

Smoking causes 120,000 deaths a year, accounting for a third of all cancer deaths and one in six other deaths. Among the health problems are lung, mouth and throat cancer, heart attacks, lung disease, cataracts, hip fractures and gum disease.

The report, released yesterday on National No Smoking Day, is expected to reinforce demands from anti-smoking campaigners for tough measures in a policy paper on smoking reduction due out later this year.

The scientists on the tobacco and health committee, led by Professor David Poswillo, have themselves produced uncompromising recommendations, with the starting point that the 'enormous damage to health and life arising

By Jenny Hope, Medical Correspondent

from smoking should no longer be accepted'.

They say: 'There is an urgency with the smoking problem that needs to be recognised by both the Government and the public.'

Restrictions on smoking in public places are needed to protect public health and it should not be allowed in public service buildings and on public transport, other than in designated areas, the report says.

Wherever possible, it should be banned in the workplace.

It says the Government should make the tobacco industry accept smoking is a major cause of premature death and there should be better disclosure of the hazards to consumers.

Awareness of the risks of smoking in the home, especially to children, should also be increased.

It recommends raising the real price of tobacco each year to discourage smoking, especially by young people, and banning all tobacco advertising, promotion and sponsorship.

And it says nicotine replacement therapy should be more widely available, possibly through NHS prescription.

Anti-smoking campaigners said the report scuppered claims by tobacco firms that a World Health Organisation report had found no extra lung cancer risk for passive smokers.

The WHO has already accused the tobacco industry of staging a publicity stunt which was 'wholly misleading' about the conclusion of its study that a link does exist.

Chief Medical Officer Sir Kenneth Calman said the Government accepted the report and hinted its recommendations might be adopted in the forthcoming policy paper.

Dr Sandy Macara, chairman of the British Medical Association, said the tobacco industry should 'hang its corporate head in shame', adding: 'Its desperate attempts to escape responsibility have been trounced.'

But John Carlisle of the Tobacco Manufacturers' Association said the report's conclusions on environmental tobacco smoke were weak and inconclusive and did not justify further curbs in public places.

The price they pay

For the passive smoker	For the smoker
Raises risk of lung cancer by 20-30%.	Causes 120,000 deaths a year.
Raises risk of heart disease by 23 per cent.	Causes 30,000 lung cancer deaths a year.
Doubles the chances of a baby of sudden infant death syndrome when the mother smokes.	Lifelong smokers have a 15 times greater risk of disease.
Increases baby's risk of respiratory illness by 50%.	Doubles the risk of dying before 65.
Gives school children a 50-60% increased chance of developing asthma.	Raises risk of a range of cancers.
Raises risk of children having 'glue ear'	Raises risk of heart attacks.
	Raises risk of cataracts.
	Raises risk of hip fractures through bone thinning.
	Smoking in pregnancy raises risk of miscarriage and low birth weight.

Source: The Daily Mail, March 1998

9

Family cut off from the fun

Social activities for Bob and Heather Conder's family revolve around other people's smoking habits.

Their two sons Keith, 13, and Clive, 11, have asthma and their breathing problems are triggered by exposure to cigarette smoke.

'As a family we can't go to places where they might be affected although it's a bit hard on our 12-year-old daughter Sarah who doesn't have asthma' said Mr Conder, 43, who works for BT near his home outside Exeter, Devon. 'There are pubs, clubs and restaurants we'd like to visit together but we can't take the risk.' Keith's medication has been changed to try to improve his condition and it seems to work. 'But our social activities are limited by smokers – their behaviour affects our behaviour. At wedding receptions, for example, when smokers move in we have to move out and sit in corners, looking anti-social. Even at the squash club we all belong to there can be a problem with people lighting up. A ban on smoking in public places is long overdue.'

© *The Daily Mail*
March, 1998

Passive smoke row

Tobacco lobby say it brings no extra risk of lung cancer

A war of words erupted between tobacco companies and anti-smoking campaigners yesterday, following a claim that passive smoking is not linked to lung cancer.

Tobacco group BAT industries have pointed to a confidential report by the World Health Organisation which they say shows there is no extra lung cancer risk for those who regularly breathe in others' cigarette smoke.

But many scientists and anti-smoking campaigners claimed that the tobacco lobby had seized on the report in a desperate bid to confuse the public and dismissed suggestions that the WHO report was being suppressed because its conclusions were potentially embarrassing.

This Thursday the Government's own Scientific Committee on Smoking and Health is expected to reveal that breathing other people's smoke raises the risk of lung cancer, heart disease, asthma and respiratory illnesses among children.

The row comes during preparations for Wednesday's No Smoking Day and a crackdown on smoking in public places. There has been hot debate on the issue since entertainer Roy Castle died in 1994 from cancer he claimed was caused by years of inhaling smoke while performing in pubs and clubs.

Sir Richard Doll – who first established the link between smoking and cancer – said that the claims about the World Health Organisation report, which looked at results from seven countries, were untrue.

By Jenny Hope, Medical Correspondent

'I know about the study because with a colleague I have contributed data from British research,' said Sir Richard, who works at the Imperial Cancer Research Fund unit at Oxford.

'The overall findings do show a link but it is not statistically significant. It is completely unjustifiable to draw the conclusion there is no link. It looks as though the increase in risk is around 20 per cent for a non-smoker living with a smoker.'

The data from Britain came from research in Devon and Cornwall which showed an increased risk of eleven to 12 per cent.

'There have been more than 40 studies now and when you put them all together the results are highly significant,' he added.

Only six months ago, research in the *British Medical Journal* said smokers living with non-smokers were 25 per cent more likely to contract lung cancer.

If the WHO study had failed to find a statistically significant risk, it was valid to ask whether there was any risk at all

---

Clive Bates, director of Action on Smoking and Health, said: 'We estimate that 600 of the 30,000 smoking-related lung cancer deaths that occur each year in Britain are caused by passive smoking. If an industrial gas caused the deaths of 600 people each year there would be an outcry against the chemical industry.'

But Dr Chris Proctor, head of Science for BAT industries, the tobacco group, said that if the WHO study had failed to find a statistically significant risk, it was valid to ask whether there was any risk at all.

No one was available at the WHO to comment yesterday.

Pay to help us quit, firms told

Three-quarters of all smokers want the tobacco industry to pay up to help them quit the habit, a survey revealed today.

A poll of 2,725 smokers found that 72 per cent thought the industry should be funding nicotine patches and clinics to help people give up smoking and a third wanted the industry to be directly liable for the cost of smoking-related illnesses. A quarter also wanted to see an increase in the price of cigarettes.

Almost half called on the Government to do more, but new research from York University shows that the Government already spends £1.83 a year per smoker to help them quit.

© *The Daily Mail*
March, 1998

The sun and your skin

Some people say that a suntan looks attractive and makes you feel healthy. But when you consider that it fades quickly and can cause permanent damage and early ageing, is it really worth it?

The truth about a suntan

Skin cancer is caused by over-exposure to ultraviolet (UV) rays – which can come from the sun or from a sunbed. Your skin darkens or tans only because it has been damaged – there is no such thing as a safe or healthy tan. Although most skin cancers are treatable, this normally involves surgery, which can be painful and disfiguring.

The wrinkle factor

Exposure to UV rays causes the outer layer of the skin (the epidermis) to thicken as more cells are produced, causing wrinkles. The elastic tissue of the skin also breaks down resulting in sags and bags. On top of this, the sun tends to dry the skin out, making it coarse and leathery. Dark patches or liver spots can appear due to the over-production of melanin (a pigment produced by skin cells). This is normally seen in older people, but can also be found in young people who sunbathe frequently.

Who's at risk?

Skin colour is a major factor in a person's risk of skin cancer. People with pale or freckled skin, fair or red hair and blue eyes are most at risk. People with darker hair and eyes who tend to tan easily are at medium risk, and those with black or brown skin that virtually never burns are at the lowest risk.

The best way to stay looking young and beautiful is to take some simple precautions:

Cover up

Make a wide-brimmed hat your summer fashion accessory. Dress to protect this summer with loose-fitting clothing. Longer sleeves will cover more of your body. The loose fit will also help you to keep cool.

Move into the shade around midday

The sun is at its hottest from around

11am to 3pm, so move into the shade (whether natural shade or not) during these hours. Plan any indoor activities for the middle of the day.

Take care not to burn

Remember that you can still get sunburnt on a cloudy or overcast day – don't be fooled by cooling winds.

Use a high-factor sunscreen

Apply a sunscreen with an SPF of 15 or above. Spread liberally and re-apply often. If you are swimming, look out for a waterproof lotion.

After-sun care

It is a good idea to use a moisturiser or body lotion if your skin has had a lot of sun, although this will not repair damaged skin it may help to remoisturise dry areas.

There are more than 40,000 new cases of skin cancer in the UK every year with over 2000 deaths – and it's on the increase.

Most cases can be avoided easily if you take it easy in the sun.

• The above information is from the Health Education Authority campaign, Sun Know How.

© Health Education Authority (HEA)
1998

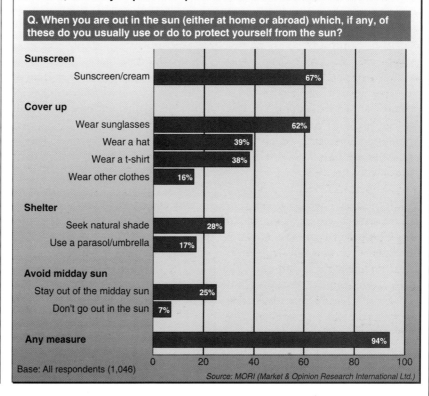

Attitudes to sunbathing

A recent MORI poll of the Cancer Research Campaign shows that three-quarters think it fine to sunbathe as long as they protect their skin from sunburn, but only a quarter expressed concerns about skin cancer.

Q. When you are out in the sun (either at home or abroad) which, if any, of these do you usually use or do to protect yourself from the sun?

Category	Measure	Percentage
Sunscreen	Sunscreen/cream	67%
Cover up	Wear sunglasses	62%
	Wear a hat	39%
	Wear a t-shirt	38%
	Wear other clothes	16%
Shelter	Seek natural shade	28%
	Use a parasol/umbrella	17%
Avoid midday sun	Stay out of the midday sun	25%
	Don't go out in the sun	7%
Any measure		94%

Base: All respondents (1,046)

Source: MORI (Market & Opinion Research International Ltd.)

Skin cancer

The facts

Sun know how

- Over 40,000 people in the UK are diagnosed with skin cancer every year, and around 2,000 people die because of it.
- It is the second most common cancer in the country.
- Over the past 15 years the incidence has doubled and continues to rise.
- Most skin cancers are curable but treatment usually involves surgery which can be disfiguring.
- Currently, fewer than 1 in 20 of those with skin cancer will die from it, and treatment is improving all the time.

Doctors have identified several different types of skin cancer. The most important distinction is between malignant melanoma and non-melanoma skin cancer.

Malignant melanoma

Malignant melanoma is the least common and the most dangerous type of skin cancer. In 1989 there were more than 4,000 new cases – approximately 1 in every 10 skin cancers. Yet as recently as 1974, there were only 1,700 cases. While the number of cases of all types of skin cancer have risen rapidly over the past 15 years, the highest increase is for melanoma.

Not only is malignant melanoma on the increase in the UK, it is rising world-wide among white populations, so much so that many scientists are now talking about a melanoma epidemic.

While the cause of melanoma is not fully understood, it is thought to be linked to occasional exposure to short periods of intense burning sunlight – such as at weekends or on holiday. This type of skin cancer is more common in indoor than outdoor workers. Melanoma is more prevalent in women than men and while most cancers are diseases of middle-age and later, melanoma is one of the most common cancers among 20-35-year-olds.

Malignant melanomas can develop unpredictably and may spread rapidly to other parts of the body. But if recognised and treated early, chances of survival are good.

Non-melanoma

Non-melanoma skin cancers (NMSCs) have increased, from 19,000 cases in 1974 to nearly 36,000 in 1989. This rise is not as rapid as it has been for melanoma, but it still gives great cause for concern.

NMSCs are not usually fatal but may be very disfiguring. They are most often found on the face, neck, ears, forearms and hands – all parts of the body that are commonly exposed to the sun.

Unlike melanomas, NMSCs are found most often in outdoor workers and in the over-50s. Most cases are caused by a lifetime of over-exposure to the sun.

Looking out for symptoms

It's not unusual to have some moles or freckles. But watch out for any moles that change size, shape or colour, become bigger, itchy or inflamed, that weep or bleed. These may be symptoms of melanoma and should be checked by your doctor.

Avoiding skin cancer

Unlike many cancers, skin cancer is a disease that is mostly avoidable. The main cause – exposure to sunlight – is widely recognised. By taking some simple precautions in the sun, we can ensure that the rise in the number of skin cancers is brought to a halt, if not reversed.

- The above information is from the Health Education Authority campaign, Sun Know How. See page 41 for address details.

© Health Education Authority (HEA)

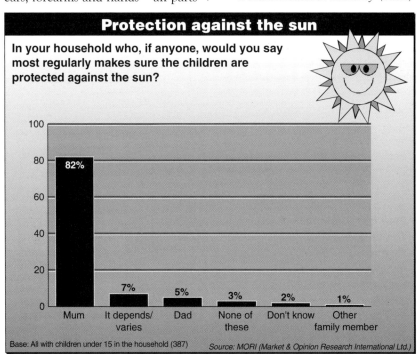

Protection against the sun

In your household who, if anyone, would you say most regularly makes sure the children are protected against the sun?

Mum	It depends/varies	Dad	None of these	Don't know	Other family member
82%	7%	5%	3%	2%	1%

Base: All with children under 15 in the household (387)

Source: MORI (Market & Opinion Research International Ltd.)

Cervical cancer research

Information from the Imperial Cancer Research Fund (ICRF)

Cervical cancer affects just over 4,000 women every year in the UK and kills about 1,400. Screening already prevents many deaths and stops even more women from getting the disease. The number of women getting and dying from cervical cancer has dropped significantly in recent years and if this trend is to continue it is essential that women carry on being screened regularly.

Screening programme

The Imperial Cancer Research Fund is carrying out research into the prevention of cervical cancer. In particular, scientists have taken an active interest in the evaluation of a computerised system for calling and recalling patients for screening and in the potential use of new tests within the National Screening Programme.

The National Cervical Screening Programme started up in March 1988 following recommendations from a report by the ICRF Co-ordinating Committee on Cervical Screening. Our researchers are now leading the evaluation project which aims to improve cervical screening by monitoring the programme and highlighting areas where changes are needed.

The percentage of women in England in the target age group of 20-64 who have had a recent smear has risen substantially since 1988 and is currently just over 84% (1993/94 data). This together with other improvements in screening should result in a substantial decrease in both the number of women getting, and the number dying, of cervical cancer over the next decade.

There already has been a substantial decrease in the number of women dying of the disease – down 30% over the past 10 years in England and Wales.

Our Mathematics, Statistics and Epidemiology (MSE) Laboratory, in conjunction with the National Screening Programme, is doing a

Imperial Cancer
Research Fund

study involving women diagnosed with cervical cancer since January 1992.

They are trying to follow the pattern of events leading to a woman's diagnosis of cervical cancer. For instance, how many smears she had, what the results were, how long ago the last smear was, if there were any previous abnormal smears and perhaps checking to make sure a previous smear was not falsely recorded as negative. It is hoped that this study will become the basis of a national audit on the performance of the screening service.

Young women

The incidence of cervical cancer rose rapidly in young women between 1960 and 1980. Cases in under-35s rose by 200% and deaths by 72%. However, it is still rare in this age group and the increases appear to have stabilised. Cervical cancer in the under-35s accounts for only 16% of cases and seven per cent of deaths.

This increase is thought to be due to changes in sexual behaviour, but smoking may play a part and there might also be other factors. The MSE Laboratory carried out a study of over 100 women under the age of 40 with invasive cervical cancer to try to identify risk factors. The researchers found the factors were similar to those in older women.

Virus

There is a link between certain types of a sexually transmitted infection called the human papilloma virus – HPV – and cervical cancer.

Recent studies have found two types to be responsible for the majority of cervix cancers.

Other factors are also involved (e.g. smoking) but HPV infection seems to be an extremely important step in the development of the disease, often occurring several years before the appearance of cancer.

Studies by the MSE Lab of the value of detecting HPV in cervical smears are currently ongoing. The team believes that the addition of a test for HPV to the current analysis of the cells taken during a smear may ultimately save up to 500 extra lives a year in this country.

But HPV infections are extremely common and the vast majority of women who have an HPV infection will not develop cervical cancer. So additional research is required to identify those who are most at risk and would benefit from treatment.

A consortium, which includes researchers from ICRF and other institutes, has recently been set up to co-ordinate work on a vaccine against one type of HPV.

Our Cancer Epidemiology Unit in Oxford has also investigated the roles played by viruses in cervical cancer. The researchers looked at the links between a herpes simplex virus and other sexually transmitted infections and this cancer. They found these conditions play little or no role.

Smoking

Researchers have consistently found an association between cervical cancer and smoking. One possible mechanism for this association is that smoking weakens the immune system's ability to eliminate HPV.

Doctors in the MSE Lab have shown that early abnormalities on the cervix of a woman who smokes are much more likely to get smaller or disappear within six months if the woman stops smoking than if she continues.

Prevention

To help prevent cervical cancer all women who have ever been sexually active should:

1) Have regular smear tests. It is important for all women to be screened at least once every five years, preferably every three.
2) Try not to smoke.
3) Be careful about the number of sexual partners they have and the number of sexual partners her partner's have had.
4) Use a condom in addition to her usual method of contraception if in doubt about her partner, or for casual relationships.

Becoming sexually active at a young age may increase a girl's risk of developing cervical cancer.

Women who have been sexually active, but are not any longer, should still go for screening if they are under 65 years old. Cervical cancer often takes 10 to 20 years to develop.

NB: If a woman develops cervical cancer it does not mean that she or her partner is promiscuous. It only takes one contact with an infected person for HPV to be transmitted and this could be more than 20 years before cancer develops.

• The above information is from the web site of the Imperial Cancer Research Fund, which can be found at http://www.lif.icnet.uk/

© Imperial Cancer Research Fund
December, 1998

Cervical cancer deaths fall by 40 per cent

By David Fletcher,
Health Correspondent

Deaths from cervical cancer have fallen by 40 per cent since 1979 as increasing numbers of women take regular smear tests, a report by the NHS cervical screening programme said yesterday.

Deaths fell to 4.1 per 100,000 women in 1995 compared with seven per 100,000 in 1979 and numbers were dropping at an accelerating rate.

'The Health of the Nation target for reducing the incidence of cervical cancer among women has been reached several years ahead of schedule,' said the report.

It said the incidence of cervical cancer in England and Wales had fallen from 16.1 new cases per 100,000 women in 1986 to 11.2 in 1993 – ahead of the target figure of 12.8 by the year 2000.

'The most likely explanation for this is the major improvements which have been brought about in the NHS screening programme,' it said.

The figures are given in new guidelines on screening for doctors and emphasise the overall success of the programme in saving lives despite a number of recent reports of women being recalled for repeat smears because of doubts about the original test.

Dr Ian Duncan, the consultant gynaecologist who drew up the report, said individual cases were tragic but the number of women affected by errors was tiny compared with the four million women who had an accurate screening examination each year.

The programme is proving so successful that Dr Duncan said they were moving towards longer intervals for some women and shorter intervals for others if they could find better ways of identifying women at low and high risk of cervical cancer. One suggestion is screening for the human papilloma virus which is found in 90 per cent of women who develop cervical cancer.

Women are currently screened at least every five years from the age of 20 to 65 but Dr Duncan said these ages could now be relaxed slightly in the light of experience gained over 20 years of screening.

The report recommends that women should have their first test between the age of 20-25 instead of immediately after their 20th birthday.

The new recommendation follows the finding that in 1996 there were no deaths from cervical cancer among teenagers and only five of the 1,329 deaths were in women under the age of 25.

At the other end of the scale, studies in Scotland found that only one in a hundred women between the age of 50-60 had an abnormal smear result.

According to the guidelines: 'Women should continue to be included in the cervical screening programme as at present, having their exit smear no more than five years before their 65th birthday.

'Studies should continue to examine further the issue of whether the upper age limit for screening could be safely lowered.'

The guidelines recommend that the interval between screening examinations should not be less than three years and not more than four and a half years after a previous negative smear.

At present about 15 per cent of women fail to turn up for screening despite repeated invitations.

© Telegraph Group Limited,
London 1998

Cervical screening

Information from Women's Nationwide Cancer Control Campaign (WNCCC)

The WNCCC encourages women between the ages of 20–64 to take part in the NHS Cervical Screening Programme and have a regular smear test. Individuals are advised on the relevance of the test.

Some facts and figures about cervical screening and cervical cancer (the cervix is the neck of the womb).

- Cervical smear tests aim to detect pre-cancerous changes – not cancer.
- In 1988 the United Kingdom introduced a comprehensive cervical screening programme.[1]
- 'The Health of the Nation' target was to reduce the incidence of invasive cervical cancer by at least 20% by the year 2000 – a target rate of 12.8 per 100,000 women.[2] The incidence of cervical cancer fell from 16.1 per 100,000 women in 1986 to 11.2 per 100,000 women in 1993[3]. ('The Health of the Nation' document is currently being revised in the government's discussion paper, 'Our Healthier Nation').
- There was a 13% decrease in the number of registrations of cancer of the cervix from 4310 in 1990, 3768 in 1991 and 3597 in 1992.[4]
- Deaths from cervical cancer in England and Wales have fallen from 1485 in 1993 to 1369 in 1994. This is a decrease of 116. The fall in mortality rate is now running at about 7% per year.[5] In 1996 1315 women died from cervical cancer.[6]
- The target coverage for screening women is 80%.[7]
- The figures released for 1996-1997 showed 84.6 per cent of women aged between 25 and 64 in England had been screened at least once in the previous five years.
- Coverage was less than 70 per cent in only two districts.[8]
- All women aged 20 to 64 years old and who are registered with a GP will be called for regular smear

tests. Some districts recall women every five years. 40% of districts screen every three years.[9] The National Audit Office supports the view that districts should ensure that they are screening a high proportion of women regularly before moving to a more frequent screening cycle.[10]

- In 1996/97, 3.8 million women were tested in England. Just fewer than eight per cent of the smears were inadequate specimens. Of the adequate smears, 91.4% were negative. 8.6% were abnormal, the breakdown of these is as follows: 6.9% borderline changes or mild dyskaryosis; 1.6% moderate or severe dyskaryosis; and 0.1% suspected invasive cancer or glandular neoplasia.[11]
- Women over 64 who have never had a smear and have ever had sexual intercourse should consult with their GP.
- A woman over the age of 64 years old can stop having a cervical smear test if the previous two smears in the last ten years were negative.[12]
- Smoking increases the risk of cervical cancer.
- The presence of the wart virus is also thought to be a risk factor.
- Using a barrier form of contraception, i.e. the cap or the condom can reduce the risk of abnormal cervical cell changes as it protects the cervix

For further information

If you have any further questions or would like to discuss any concerns, please contact the WNCCC.

The WNCCC produce a range of publications for order. For a full publications list and order form contact the WNCCC on 0171 729 4688. Relevant publications include: *Cervical Smear Test* leaflet, *Heath Care for the Older Woman* leaflet, *Calling all Women* leaflet (available in 10 languages: Bengali, Cantonese, English, Gujurati, Hindi, Punjabi,

Somali, Turkish, Urdu and Vietnamese.) *A Simple Check* video.

Alternatively, if you have any questions and would like to speak to someone, you may wish to contact one of the following helplines: CancerBACUP on 0808 800 1234 or Cancerlink on 0800 132905.

References.

1. E. Farmery, M. Gray. *Report of the First Five Years of the NHS Cervical Screening Programme.* Oxford: National Co-ordinating Network, 1994.
2. *The Health of the Nation – Key Area Handbook: Cancers.* Dept. of Health. Health of the Nation 1993.
3. Office for National Statistics, November 1996.
4. *Monitor Population and Health.* Office for National Statistics, 19 September 1996. P. 8.
5. NHS Cervical Screening Programme. *Links* newsletter. No. 15. P. 1.
6. Office for National Statistics, November 1996.
7. E. Farmery, M. Gray. *Report of the First Five Years of the NHS Cervical Screening Programme.* Oxford: National Co-ordinating Network, 1994. P. 5.
8. Department of Health. *Statistical Bulletin.* Cervical Screening Programme, England: 1996-1997. Bulletin 1997/27.
9. *Cervical Screening. A Pocket Guide.* NHS Cervical Screening Programme, November 1996.
10. E. Farmery, M. Gray. *Report of the First Five Years of the NHS Cervical Screening Programme.* Oxford: National Co-ordinating Network, 1994. P. 25.
11. Department of Health. *Statistical Bulletin.* Cervical Screening Programme, England: 1996-1997. Bulletin 1997/27.
12. S. Haslett. *Having a Cervical Smear.* Beconsfield Publishers. Bucks 1994.

The cancer young men ignore at their peril

Many males play down the fact that unusual symptoms could be cancerous – and delay is dangerous. Christine Doyle reports

David Brown discovered the pea-sized lump in his groin while he was taking a shower. His initial reaction was to ignore it and hope it would go away.

'I was only 28 and, although I am quite open about intimate subjects, I put it to the back of my mind. I don't think I did it out of fear – it was more disbelief,' he says.

Initially there was no discomfort, but as the lump in his right testicle slowly swelled, David developed pains in his back. Even then he did nothing. He convinced himself that the pains were due to sciatica and would soon clear up.

But, 17 months after he had first noticed the growth, his back pain was so intense that, in the middle of the night, his three flatmates took him to an accident and emergency department.

Tests revealed that he not only had cancer in his testes but that cancerous growths had spread to his spine. Because of the delay, his treatment and recovery took almost two years and included major back surgery. 'My parents were told I would die, so I consider myself extremely lucky to be alive,' he says.

His story is not unusual. Testicular cancer is a young man's disease; it is most common between the ages of 20 and 35 and is on the increase. According to a Mori survey conducted recently for the Institute of Cancer Research, only one in five men claim to know much about the illness; indeed, most men actually know more about women's cancers than their own.

For this reason, Everyman, a charity set up by the institute, has designated June the first Male Cancer Awareness month. Cancer campaigners say that, despite progress, men are more than 15 years behind women in health self-awareness and general knowledge. In one study, some men believed women could get prostrate cancer. Yet, unlike any women's cancer, male cancer of the testes is almost 100 per cent curable – if caught before it has spread.

Understanding precisely why many men still react so slowly to swelling, pain or body changes is crucial if they are to be persuaded to take prompt action. According to Professor Alan Horwich of the Royal Marsden Hospital, there is, on average, a three-month delay before men report suspicious symptoms to a GP.

'Most of this is accounted for by what I call optimistic denial by young men, who expect to be healthy.

There is a natural wish, when something is slightly abnormal, to look on it as trivial. The trouble is that a proportion do not report for nine to 12 months and, by then, the cancer is well advanced.'

Prof. Tim Oliver, who heads the Men's Cancer Unit at St Bartholomew's Hospital in London, says: 'In one week, recently, I had two patients who had put off seeing their GP for more than a year. They will recover, but their treatment will take longer and be much tougher, involving chemotherapy, radiotherapy and more operations than if they had come earlier.'

Late treatment usually means more side-effects. David still has serious back pain caused by post-operative scar tissue, and this has affected his mobility. Infertility is a possibility, although, these days, most men are asked before treatment if they want sperm to be frozen as an insurance policy.

Single men are the least likely to seek early treatment because there is no wife or lover to chivvy them into seeing their GP.

Another problem, according to Colin Pavitt, 36, who is being treated at St Bartholomew's for cancer which has spread to his lungs, is that many men are not accustomed to 'examining themselves intimately, let alone asking a doctor to do so'.

Colin rejected his wife's urging to consult his GP about a painful swelling in his groin. 'I thought I had banged myself or had a minor infection,' he says. 'One testicle had always been a little uncomfortable.'

Colin left it a year before seeking medical attention, by which time the cancer had infiltrated the lymph glands behind his stomach and lungs.

Prof. Oliver has reassured him that he will be clear of cancer by October. 'I believe him, but I wish I had not waited so long,' Colin says.

Another patient at St Bartholo-mew's, Colin Osborne, who had testicular cancer four years ago at the age of 32, has set up the Orchid Cancer Appeal, to provide informa-tion and to raise money for research.

He thinks men find it depressing and embarrassing to talk about cancer and other health matters. 'One problem is that the word "testicle" is still seen as naughty, and testicular cancer is a taboo subject, unlike breast cancer.'

David Brown agrees. 'We have to demystify the word. I know guys who have been to a doctor with a lump down there, but end up talking about a raging sore throat.'

The GPs themselves are not entirely blameless. Clare Moynihan, senior medical researcher at the institute, says: 'Time and again, men told me they had seen their GP but were sent away without being examined. Such men may well be reluctant to return to the doctor and could leave it too late.'

Phil Williams, another cured patient, who founded the national helpline Mind Over Matter, quotes the case of a young man who had a severe relapse because his GP insisted that his discomfort and swelling were due to an infection. 'The trouble is that most people do not challenge their doctors: they assume they are always right.'

For many men, the need to remove a testicle is sexually under-mining, and that in itself can lead to delay. However, Moynihan's research provides good news. 'Wives and girlfriends usually do not worry about this, and single men generally have no difficulty starting a new relationship. With time, many even turn down the offer of a replacement artificial testicle.'

So, can we expect to see more forceful campaigning from men? If this were breast cancer month, you

would know it from a flowering of pink ribbons on a million lapels. This first men's cancer month has yet to spark mass interest, though the outlook is promising.

Members of Parliament have just launched the first all-party parliamentary group to look into issues surrounding male cancers. Men's magazines, such as *Men's Health*, are stirring some debate. And, according to Moynihan, the Internet has hundreds of sites devoted to health matters that are being increasingly visited by men.

'They like the anonymity,' she explains.

The brothers: a family history

Michael Beaver took no chances when, in 1989, he developed a large and painful swelling on his left testicle. He saw his GP immediately and was told it was probably water – a hydrocele – and could be treated. However, the swelling persisted and on his third visit, Michael, an accountant now aged 49, insisted on seeing a consultant.

Tests disclosed cancer and the next day a surgeon removed the

---

Cases of testicular cancer have doubled since the seventies, to around 1,500 a year – about one in 400 men will develop the disease

---

affected testicle. Michael was so insistent because his younger brother, Martin, had been treated for the same cancer 18 years previously, at the age of 25.

Martin says: 'My GP was wonderful and referred me instantly. Even so, the cancer had spread… I had a cocktail of three anti-cancer drugs and then an operation to remove lymph glands.'

Michael was luckier. 'The cancer had not spread and I was soon back at work.'

In a few cases, there is clear evidence that testicular cancer is hereditary. The son of a father with testicular cancer has a four times greater risk of developing the disease, while the brother of a sufferer has a nine times greater risk. As yet, no genes have been identified.

Rise in cases

Cases of testicular cancer have doubled since the seventies, to around 1,500 a year – about one in 400 men will develop the disease. It is most common between the ages of 20 and 35 and even though the cure rate is high, about 130 sufferers die annually. Men with undescended testes are 40 times more at risk. Those who contract mumps after puberty are also at higher risk, as are those with a low sperm count.

The reason for the increase in this male cancer remains unknown, but Prof. Tim Oliver, of St Bartho-lomew's Hospital, London, thinks simple explanations are unlikely. Some people might be more sus-ceptible to environmental influ-ences, such as exposure to female hormones in water or baby milk – this has also been linked with a rise in breast cancer in women.

A sedentary way of life has also been suggested, and diet might play a part. Among Africans and Asians, the rates are relatively low. Britain is in the middle of the European league table; the Finns have the highest rates and their Norwegian neigh-bours the lowest.

Warning signs
- A lump in either testicle
- Any enlargement
- A feeling of heaviness or firmness in scrotum

- Dull aching or dragging feeling in abdomen or groin
- Tenderness or discomfort in testicle which does not clear
- A sudden collection of fluid in the scrotum
- Enlargement or tenderness around the nipples.

Speed is the key

Twenty years ago, little could be done. But treatment with drugs which cause cancer cells to self-destruct has transformed the outlook. Today, more than nine in ten patients recover completely, with cure rates in early cases of 96 and 98 per cent. When the cancer has spread moderately, the cure rate is 80 per cent, and even when the spread is large, the cure rate is 65 per cent.

Early detection remains the key. If caught early enough, a simple operation to remove the affected testicle provides a complete cure.

Find out more

See your GP if you have any warning signs. For information or to talk with former patients: Mind Over Matter, 01703 775611; Orchid Cancer Appeal, 0181-501 3027.

Everyman Institute of Cancer Research. For leaflets on testicular self-examinations and prostrate cancer, call: 0171-352 8188.

CancerBACUP. For a free copy of *Understanding Cancer of the Testes*, send an A5 sae with 49p stamp to CancerBACUP, 3 Bath Place, Rivington Street, London EC2A 3DR. Helpline 0800 181199 or Internet www.cancerbacup.org.uk

For a leaflet on cancer genetics, send an sae to the Cancer Research Campaign, 10 Cambridge Terrace, London NW1 4JL.

Testicular cancer

Information from the Imperial Cancer Research Fund

Testicular cancer is the most common form of cancer in young men, occurring mostly in those aged between 15 and 49. However, it is still quite rare with just over 1,500 new cases a year and about 90 deaths in the UK. It is also one of the most curable cancers. Over 90% of patients make a complete recovery and when the disease is caught at an early stage survival is almost 100%.

Symptoms

The first sign of this cancer is usually a swelling of one of the testes. Occasionally there may be a dull ache or, even more seldom, acute pain. Very rarely the tumour itself may disappear and the first symptom is stomach or backache from secondary spread.

Testicular self-awareness

As with most cancers – early detection can improve the results of treatment. There is a wide variation in normal testicular size and shape, so it is important for all men from the onset of puberty to be aware of what is normal for them.

Examination is the only way to do this and is easiest in a warm bath or after a shower, when the muscle in the scrotal sac is more relaxed. Each testicle should be gently examined between the fingers and thumb of both hands. Any change

Imperial Cancer
Research Fund

(particularly a hardening, lump, or swelling) from what is normal for you should be discussed with your doctor.

Diagnosis

Your family doctor should be able to tell whether any lump is benign (the majority found by self-examination are), or if it is one of the small minority which needs urgent treatment as it may be cancerous. If this is the case you will be referred to hospital where doctors may do an ultrasound test to be sure that it is cancer.

If this test is positive the affected testicle will be removed and examined under a microscope to confirm the diagnosis. There are two main types of this cancer – teratomas and seminomas. Teratomas usually affect men aged between 15 and about 30, while seminomas are more likely to occur in men between 30 and 50 years old.

Improvements in treatment

In 1950 only 40% of patients survived. However, the last 18 years have seen dramatic progress in the treatment of testicular cancer, particularly over the past eight years

as cure rates have reached more than 90%. For many years we supported the Medical Oncology Unit at the Royal London Hospital which was involved in much of this work and made a unique contribution by developing less toxic treatments. Current priorities are to improve on this work, but also to increase the cure rate of the small number (about one in 20) who develop drug-resistant cancer.

If the cancer has not spread it may not be necessary for further treatment after surgery. If it has spread, the patient is usually given chemotherapy (drug treatment), though for a few patients radio-therapy is still used in the early stages. Occasionally at the end of treatment it may be necessary to use surgery to remove any residual lumps.

Chemotherapy

Nineteen years ago a patient with widespread testicular cancer stood very little chance of recovering. Then in the late 1970s two new drugs called cisplatin and etoposide were found to be more effective than the previously available drugs. This treatment was very successful and survival increased from about 25% to 85%.

The one disadvantage of these drugs is that they cause nausea, vomiting and temporary hair-loss.

However, the treatment has since been modified with the introduction of improved anti-sickness drugs and the side-effects are now much less severe. When the therapy stops, the side-effects disappear and the patient will return to complete normality.

Fertility

The occasional patient may have problems with infertility before diagnosis of testis cancer. For those who are fertile there is little risk of their fertility being damaged irreversibly by treatment. A period of 12-24 months of diminished fertility after treatment is, however, usual. Several hundred children have been fathered over the last decade by patients treated for testis cancer and there is no evidence of any genetic risks from treatment.

Risk factors

While the risk of dying from this cancer has decreased substantially over the past 20 years a man's risk of developing it has nearly doubled and the figures are still going up.

Men born with an undescended testicle (known as cryptorchidism) have a greater chance of developing testicular cancer. The incidence of cryptorchidism has increased 60% since 1960 and men with this condition have a five times increased risk of the disease. However, even with this increased risk it is still much rarer than, for example, a woman's risk of breast cancer.

Our Cancer Epidemiology Unit in Oxford has carried out several studies into the reasons for this increase. In one project researchers at the Unit and other colleagues looked at hormone levels in mothers whose pregnancies resulted in a child with undescended testes.

In a larger-scale study 800 men with testicular cancer and 800 without were interviewed and asked questions about potential risk factors as were the mothers who were asked for details about their pregnancy. The results showed that an early age of puberty may increase the risk of testis cancer while high levels of exercise may decrease the risk. Both these findings require confirmation, but provide a hypothesis for investigating the biological basis of this disease.

Another important finding was that boys who have an undescended testicle which is corrected below the age of 10 are no longer at an increased cancer risk. The study was funded by Imperial Cancer and the Cancer Research Campaign.

The researchers have also looked at testis cancer in families and one area of considerable importance to emerge is that there may be a hereditary factor involved. Our Tissue Antigen Laboratory is working with researchers in Leeds and London to investigate this further and have set up a register of patients with close relatives (brother or father) who have had testis cancer.

So far, the register has enabled them to establish that having a brother who develops testicular cancer may increase a man's chance of getting the disease by nearly 10 times that of the general population. However, a man's lifetime risk of the disease is only one in 450, so this means that having a brother with this cancer increases the risk to about one in 50.

The researchers are now studying these families with the aim of learning more about the genetic mechanisms involved in the development of these tumours and possible ways of reducing the risks of this cancer.

• The above is information from Imperial Cancer Research Fund. See page 41 for address details.

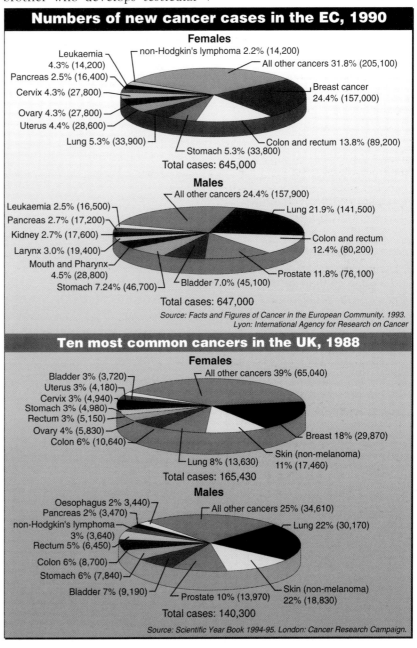

Prostate cancer

Information from the Imperial Cancer Research Fund

Prostate cancer is the third most common cancer in men with over 15,600 new cases a year in the UK. It is rare in men under 50, but after this age the incidence rises steeply – faster than any other cancer. The average age when patients are diagnosed is over 70.

Symptoms

Older men often suffer from an enlarged prostate. The condition is usually benign, but if you have one or more of the following symptoms you should see your family doctor:

- difficulty passing urine,
- passing urine more often, especially at night,
- inability to urinate,
- weak or interrupted flow of urine,
- pain or burning sensation when urinating,
- painful ejaculation,
- blood in urine or semen,
- frequent pain in the lower back, upper thighs or pelvic area.

Screening – why no national programme?

The main problem with looking at screening for prostate cancer is that this cancer varies widely in the way it develops in individual patients. When it is diagnosed it is not possible to tell whether the tumour is one which will spread very quickly or grow slowly.

Imperial Cancer Research Fund

The dilemma facing today's physicians treating prostate cancer is how to make the differentiation, and therefore be in a position to prescribe the appropriate kind of treatment. Studying the cancer's basic biology is going to be the best way to distinguish low and high risk cancers.

With our present knowledge, screening could lead to the over-treatment of a very large number of men. About 50% of those aged 70-80 years old have localised prostate cancers and the majority of these tumours would, if left alone, never become advanced cancers. Large trials will be needed to evaluate different screening and treatment approaches.

Family history

Less than five per cent of prostate cancer patients have a family history of the disease. However, in those who do the cancer can occur at a younger age and be more aggressive. Because of this, screening may be most beneficial in those with a possible inherited predisposition to the disease. If they are found to have

cancer, then radical therapy is likely to be the best treatment because the disease is more likely to be aggressive.

Treatment

There are three main stages of prostate cancer – localised, locally advanced and advanced. The treatment you receive will depend on the stage.

Localised

These cancers are usually detected through screening or by investigation for another condition and do not have symptoms. In many cases immediate treatment is not necessary and if the cancer grows slowly it may never progress to cause any problems. Other treatment options are radiotherapy and surgery and recent improvements in both these techniques mean that most patients do not suffer permanent side-effects such as incontinence and impotence.

Locally advanced

At this stage the cancer has grown, but not spread to another part of the body. Patients may receive radio-therapy or hormone therapy. Prostate cancer is a sex-hormone dependent cancer and reducing hormone levels by using drugs or surgery will help to control the cancer for several years.

Deaths from cancer — UK 1995

10 most common cancers

Men		Women	
Lung	23,562	Breast	14,114
Prostate	9,858	Lung	13,038
Bowel	9,041	Bowel	8,893
Stomach	4,818	Ovary	4,357
Oesophagus	4,056	Pancreas	3,442
Bladder	3,664	Stomach	3,187
Pancreas	3,078	Oesophagus	2,608
Non-Hodgkin's lymphoma	2,391	Non-Hodgkin's lymphoma	2,060
Leukaemia	2,177	Bladder	1,760
Kidney	1,854	Leukaemia	1,729

Total deaths (Men and Women)

Lung	36,600
Bowel	17,934
Breast	14,201
Prostate	9,858
Stomach	8,005
Oesophagus	6,664
Pancreas	6,520
Bladder	5,424
Non-Hodgkin's lymphoma	4,451
Ovary	4,357

Source: Imperial Cancer Research Fund (ICRF)

Advanced

Unfortunately, this cancer is very resistant to drugs. However, most patients will achieve one to two years' disease arrest from hormone-reducing therapy until the cancer learns to survive without hormones. Chemotherapy can sometimes help for a while after hormonal therapy fails, though it is rarely used. Radiotherapy is more helpful in relieving pain caused by cancer spreading to the bones. Trials are under way using drugs which are proving helpful in treating prostate cancer which has spread to the bones.

Treatment trials

Our Clinical Trial Service Unit (CTSU) in Oxford has been collaborating with the Medical Research Council to assess the effectiveness of various treatments.

One study – the largest European trial of prostate cancer ever done – involves 81 physicians throughout the UK and more than 900 patients. The researchers are comparing immediate versus deferred hormone therapy for locally advanced and symptomless advanced prostate cancer. They are assessing local control, delay in cancer spread and delay (if any) of death.

The CTSU is also working with the Netherlands Cancer Institute in Amsterdam on a world-wide review of prostate cancer trials, involving the central review of information on almost 20,000 men. So far, it appears that hormone treatment should start early, but that it does not need to be very intensive.

New methods of detection?

Our Nuclear Medicine Group at St Bartholomew's Hospital, London, is developing novel ways of detecting cancer spread by using radioactive antibodies which home-in on cancer cells. When the patient is put under a gamma camera, the antibodies, and therefore the cancer, show up as hot spots. This is helping doctors to see how advanced a cancer is before they operate.

New methods used by ICRF can detect microscopic cells in the blood of prostate cancer patients and are being used to assess new drug effects.

Causes

We do not know what causes prostate cancer. We know that risk increases with age and that black men are more likely to develop this cancer than white men. In fact, black men in the USA have the highest rate of prostate cancer in the world.

Researchers in our Cancer Epidemiology Unit in Oxford have been investigating links between prostate cancer and radiation.

There is some weak evidence that diet, sexual activity, and sexually transmitted diseases may be associated with risk. Other researchers in the unit are looking at these factors in detail. Six hundred people have been interviewed and the results are being analysed.

The differences in incidence between population groups are by far the most significant risk factors. Much more research is needed to explore causes and the role that genetic factors may play alongside possible environmental factors.

Laboratory research

A number of our laboratories are looking at hormones and the genes which control them and their involvement in certain hormone-responsive cancers like that of the prostate. This work may lead to clues on the reasons for drug-resistance and eventually to new therapies.

Growth factors

Scientists in our Medical Oncology Unit at the Western General Hospital, Edinburgh, in collaboration with researchers in the hospital's department of Surgery/Urology, have identified two stimulatory factors associated with the spread of prostate cancer to the bone. This work is now being continued in the hope that it might lead to a new approach in the treatment of this disease.

New genes

ICRF scientists in London and Leeds discovered PTEN, an important gene in prostate cancer and are currently studying it's diagnostic and biological value.

• The above information is from the web site of the Imperial Cancer Research Fund, which can be found at http://www.lif.icnet.uk/

© Imperial Cancer Research Fund
July, 1998

Why don't we all get cancer?

Information from the CRC Institute for Cancer Studies at the University of Birmingham

If you have read through *What Causes Cancer?* (page 2) you may be forgiven for thinking that with that number of potential causes, everyone will get cancer. But not everyone does. So why do some people get it and others don't?

The clues are all there in *What Causes Cancer?* As ever, there are a number of different factors working together:

- 'Risky' behaviour
- Genetic predisposition
- Chance
- Your immune system
- Age.

'Risky' behaviour

This just means indulging in something that increases your risk. It may be smoking, or drinking too much, or eating a very unhealthy diet. Some of us look after ourselves better than others. And this can have a real effect on our health. But some people look after themselves really well and still get cancer. While others don't seem to look after themselves at all and never do.

Genetic predisposition

You may hear doctors or scientists talk about genetic predisposition to cancer. This means your genetic make-up makes it more likely that you will develop cancer.

There are such things as cancer families. That is, families who have a much higher incidence of cancer amongst their members than one would normally expect. This may be particular types of cancer. But some families have all sorts of different cancers turning up in their family tree. They probably have a mutation in a gene that is crucial in the development of many different cancers. Researchers often ask such families to help them in their research. Their genetic make-up provides clues that help show which genes are the most important in causing cancer.

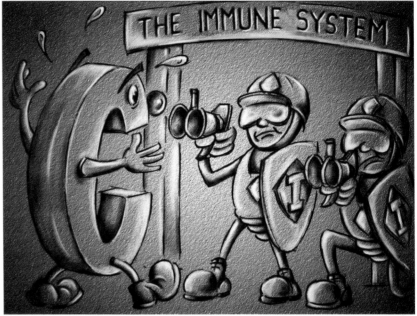

For most people who may have a general susceptibility to getting cancer, then it is not that obvious. Many of us probably have particular genes that are not that important in cancer development, but may increase our risk a little. For example, the cells of the respiratory system may be more likely to be damaged by cigarette smoke for person 'A' compared to person 'B'. It is more likely that person 'A' will develop a cancer than person 'B' who does not have that affected gene.

Cancer specialists believe that the younger someone is when they develop an 'adult' cancer, the more likely it is that there are genetic factors at work.

Chance

Many changes in genes are accidental. Cells divide and each time they do, they have to copy their genetic code completely. Sometimes mistakes happen. Many of these would be fatal and cause the daughter cell to die.

Some wouldn't make that much difference to how the cell worked. But they may take that cell one step further along the road to becoming cancerous.

Very many people with cancer, and their families, find this aspect of their disease very difficult to come to terms with. It somehow makes cancer easier to deal with if you understand why you have it.

Your immune system

The balance between the immune system and cancer is complicated. There is more about this in the section on the immune system in *What Causes Cancer?*, within our web site. See below for web site address details.

Age

Some doctors say that if all men lived long enough they would get prostate cancer. It is true that the longer we live, the more likely we are to gather enough genetic damage to start a cancer off. Some of us just die of something else before we get to that point.

• The above is an extract from the CRC Institute for Cancer Studies web site, which can be found at http://medweb.bham.ac.uk/cancerhelp/

Close relationships and cancer

Information from Cancerlink

What is cancer?

Our bodies are made up of millions of cells. Usually, new cells grow to replace old, worn cells and this process is carefully controlled. Sometimes, for reasons which are not fully understood, the controlling mechanism seems to break down. More cells grow than are needed and they are not quite the same as normal cells. Eventually, there are enough of these extra cells to form a growth, or tumour.

The word cancer describes a type of disease that occurs when some of the body's cells start to behave in this uncontrolled way.

There are many kinds of cancer. What might seem to be the same cancer in two people may, in fact, be quite different. Doctors do a number of tests to find out what kind of cancer someone has and which treatment is best for them.

You can find out more about any aspect of cancer or its treatment from Cancerlink's Freephone Cancer Information Helpline on 0800 132905.

What is closeness?

'Communication is a very important part of a close relationship and so is sharing feelings. For me, both of these matter more than a sexual relationship.'

Most people want to love and be loved. It makes us feel good about ourselves and helps us not to feel alone. Close relationships with partners, friends, parents or children give us a sense of ourselves and a feeling of being connected with other people.

Closeness, or intimacy, is about knowing other people and also about knowing ourselves. Some people who have had cancer feel that their experience has helped them to get to know themselves much better, and through this they have found new strengths and weaknesses. They often feel that they have learned to show more of what they feel and think to their partners, families and friends.

The cancer journey

'I felt very alert, very aware and very annoyed when I received my diagnosis. I was also worried about change – so worried that I wouldn't ask about it. I needed to be in control.'

'My diagnosis was a huge shock. My biggest fear was that I wasn't going to be able to carry on providing for everyone.'

'I slowly began to rediscover the "me" that had somehow become eroded in the frantic years of being mum, wife and carer. I'm a very different person now. The ripples go out to my family and friends, exposing them to change too. I have sorted out my priorities.'

Some people have described their experience of cancer as a journey. They travel to a place they have never visited before, alone or with a close companion. They face danger and uncertainty. They feel joy and fulfilment. They find new strengths and abilities. They cry and laugh.

On the way, they meet new friends who are on a similar journey and they give and receive support. As they learn to take control, their route becomes more familiar and easier to navigate. They do not know where their journey will end, nor what else will happen along the way, but for many it is a chance to discover more about themselves and the people close to them, so it can be very rewarding.

When someone is diagnosed with cancer they may feel angry, disbelieving, frightened, sad, guilty, vulnerable, desperate or lonely. These same feelings may come and go at particular times in their cancer journey, such as during treatment, months after treatment and at check-up times. At different stages of the cancer journey, everyone involved may feel overwhelmed, helpless and frightened. A Cancerlink booklet, *Life with cancer*, may be helpful during this time.

For other people, a diagnosis brings some relief, particularly if they've been feeling unwell for some time. Even if you and those close to you know that something is wrong, you may have felt that others didn't believe you, including your doctors. This can be very upsetting, so a diagnosis of cancer may bring the relief of knowing that it all makes sense.

There may be points in your cancer journey when you need time on your own to absorb what has happened to you, or you may want company because you feel very alone. Some people completely rediscover themselves through their experience.

The cancer journey may help you not only to get to know yourself better but also to think again about your close relationships. Are they what you want them to be? Are you who you want to be in them?

Living with uncertainty

Cancer can throw everyone involved into a whirlpool of emotion. Sometimes you're in the middle of the whirlpool, feeling overwhelmed and unable to cope. At other times, it's as though you're on the bank where it's calmer, but any extra stress can hurl you back into the middle again. People with long-term, chronic conditions often find that there are times of crisis and times of calm. The person with the illness and those around them learn to live with uncertainty.

'The idea of hooking yourself up to somebody who has a chronic illness which could be life-threatening is a big deal. I appear to be very well, but I know that at any time I could become extremely ill. I don't even know what it would be like for myself, let alone for my partner or potential partner.'

Because cancer can be life-threatening, most people who are affected by it need closeness, affection, caring and support. Many people feel that, in having cancer, they've let their partner, friend or family down.

'I was extremely sad at what I

considered I had done to my partner by having cancer, because it felt like I had let her down. I got home from hospital and just couldn't stop crying. I didn't even know if I was going to be a part of bringing my children up.'

'I find that when I get close to someone new, the fact that I have cancer is a huge barrier. I feel I'm going to let them down because I'm going to die, and it isn't fair.'

Intimacy means not only knowing yourself but feeling safe and trusting enough to allow another person to know you too, whether they are a friend, a family member or a partner. Getting close to another person is never easy and cancer brings extra pressures which affect close relationships.

People often find that some of their friends are not able to cope with their diagnosis, but others come into their lives quite unexpectedly.

'I think the gift of cancer has been that it has given me a chance to see the real me, whether I liked what I saw or not.'

'I found I had two sorts of friends. There were those who immediately treated me as if I was dead and didn't want to have anything to do with it. They felt awkward and completely cut themselves off. But others saw it as a challenge, although I hardly knew some of them. They felt that we were all in this together, that my cancer was something we had to fight and they were going to help me fight. There's just no way that you can know, at the outset, who's going to be there for you and who's not.'

Most people who have cancer want someone there for them – a person they can trust and talk to. It's not always clear at the beginning of the cancer journey who that will be for you.

Stress

Everyone affected by cancer has to deal with extra stress on top of normal, everyday worries. Cancer puts great pressure on relationships by affecting people's roles at home, or their ability to hold down a job and keep up their financial and other contributions to their household.

People with cancer often find that they are so worried about painful or disfiguring treatment, trying to keep things 'normal' at home or at work, and the fear of dying, that they have little energy left for anything else. The people closest to them may resent the way their lives have been disrupted. Try to talk with each other about how things have changed and how you and your partner, family or friends will deal with that change.

At first you may need to have time alone.

'I wanted to face the possibility alone until my diagnosis was confirmed. It helped me to prepare for the worst, to pamper myself in little ways, to be quiet and leisurely about what to do and when to do it. Why shouldn't I stand by the window for half an hour watching the sun come up, and then go back to bed with a cuppa?'

Worrying can also have a serious effect on how well you sleep. Yet sleep is vital in helping you cope with stress and giving you the stamina you need if you are supporting someone close to you, either practically or emotionally, for any length of time.

'Don't be afraid to go and talk to your GP if you have trouble sleeping. He or she may be able to give you something that will help on a short-term basis.'

Conflict

Stress often leads to arguments between people who are close, and relationships which were already in difficulties can be destroyed by the extra anxiety that cancer brings. It is normal to be angry with each other at a time of great worry, but often neither of you feels you have the right to say how angry you are. You may find that you fight about small things, or that you bottle up your anger until you finally explode, causing a huge row. Try to notice when tension is building up and see if you can work out the root of the problem between you.

'I was taking time to consider whether to have a bone marrow transplant and my sister was a possible donor. My mother said I was being selfish to take so long to make up my mind, as I was affecting my sister's life. But because I was the one facing a life-and-death operation, I had to be absolutely sure it was right. There was so much hidden and unspoken in that argument. I was really bitter.'

There is no 'right way' to be angry and it's not always possible to avoid conflict. Understanding the real cause of your anger is a good start, and having a clear idea of what others need from you and whether you are willing or able to give it. Sometimes close relationships can become even closer when they are secure enough for people to be angry and resentful about the changes that are taking place without risking the relationship itself.

Depression

When people get very stressed or overwhelmed by physical illness and treatment, they often become depressed. This is made worse if there is no one to talk to. Sometimes friends, partners and family members are dealing with their own reactions and cannot be of much help to the person who has cancer.

'When the doctor gave me the diagnosis, this really odd expression came over my husband's face. I guess it was shock, but it sort of said, "You're dead". And from then onwards, that's how he behaved.'

Depression is very common and you may find it helpful to talk to somebody who is not involved at all. Cancerlink can give you details of your local cancer support group, or you can just ring them for a chat. There may also be somebody at your local GP's surgery or hospital who is trained as a counsellor and works with people affected by cancer.

Body image

Your body image is the way you see yourself physically and how you believe others see you. People with cancer may not feel as good about themselves as they used to, because the way they look has changed, or they feel it has changed.

A number of things can make people look or feel different, including surgery, treatments, stress and feeling unwell for a long period. There may be no noticeable change on the outside but people feel different on the inside, which is just as important.

Many people who have changed, emotionally or physically, avoid any kind of closeness. For example, a woman who has had breast surgery may no longer feel attractive and desirable. A man with a colostomy bag may worry about leakage or smell. By rejecting the people closest to you, you avoid being rejected yourself. But if you avoid talking about your real feelings and fears, it can lead to misunderstandings, which in turn can cause resentment.

It can help to talk about any changes and to say how you feel about them and how they're affecting your relationship. Talking often helps people feel less frightened and isolated. You may find it useful to read a Cancerlink booklet called *Body image, sexuality and cancer*. Talking to others who have had similar experiences may also help to show you that there is a way through these feelings.

Finance

Another way in which cancer causes stress is by threatening financial security. If someone has to stop work because they have cancer, or to care for a relative or partner with cancer, their income will drop. Single people who are solely responsible for the running of their home may be under huge financial pressure, with the extra costs of travelling to hospital, taking time off work and heating their homes all day, every day.

Talk to your hospital social worker or local Citizens' Advice Bureau as early as you can about possible changes in your financial situation. Cancerlink's booklet *Cancer and employment* will give you further information. You can also find out about grants or benefits that may be available by phoning Cancerlink.

• The above is an extract from *Close relationships and cancer*, produced by Cancerlink. See page 41 for address details.

© Cancerlink

Mobile phones 'could be to blame for cancer surge'

Doctors suspect mobile phones are behind a huge increase in brain tumours in Australia.

Over the ten years that the devices became popular, cases soared more than 60 per cent in women and by 50 per cent in men, according to a study.

The disturbing results of the research have prompted cancer specialist Dr Andrew Davidson to ask Australia's biggest phone company, Telstra, to co-operate in research to determine whether there is a link between mobiles and the disease.

Studies in Australia and the US showed that the phones sent radiation into the brains of mice and rats, causing cancer, short-term memory loss and lapses in concentration. Following the death of

By Richard Shears in Sydney

one mobile phone user – American heart surgeon Dr Dean Rittmann – his family have started legal action against the manufacturer. They claim his illness was caused by radiation emitted from his phone.

The World Health Organisation has already called for more international research into whether the devices might cause diseases including cancer.

Dr Davidson, who is based at Fremantle Hospital, says Western Australia's cancer registry shows brain tumours in men and women increased significantly over the period during which mobile phones became popular. The frequency of

tumours in every 100,000 people was 6.4 for men and 4.0 for women in 1982, rising to 9.6 for men and 6.5 for women a decade later.

'The assumption is that the rise is related to the use of analogue phones in the late 1980s,' said Dr Davidson.

He added that there was evidence from around the country that brain cancers were on the increase.

They had risen from six to eight in every 100,000 people between 1982 and 1992.

The Australian government has already launched a five-year study into the potential health dangers from mobile phones and related equipment, including transmission towers.

© *The Daily Mail*
January, 1998

More beat cancer, but UK trails other countries for cures

By Amelia Gentleman

Cancer survival rates have improved significantly in England and Wales since 1980, but remain among the worst in the western world, according to figures.

The proportion of patients surviving more than five years after diagnosis rose from 25 per cent to 30 per cent. But the degree of improvement varies widely according to the type of cancer, with only limited advances made in some of the most common and dangerous – including lung cancer. Survival rates still trail behind those in many other European countries and the US.

The study, conducted by the Imperial Cancer Research Fund with the Office of National Statistics, compared five-year survival figures for 370,000 patients diagnosed in 1981 and 1989. A patient who survives more than five years is classified as cured.

Gillian Reeves, co-author of the report, said: 'About 200,000 people in England and Wales were diagnosed with cancer in 1989 and 60,000 of them survived. This is about 10,000 more than would have survived according to 1981 figures.' Breast cancer sufferers now stand a much improved chance of full recovery (with survival rates up from 61 per cent to 68 per cent), as do people with bowel cancer (32 to 39 per cent), non-Hodgkin's lymphoma (35 to 42 per cent) and leukaemia (21 to 27 per cent).

But improvements in the treatment and diagnosis of lung cancer have been marginal – with only 4 per cent of sufferers diagnosed in 1989 likely to survive, just a small improvement on the 1981 figures. Dr Reeves said: 'The cancers showing an increase in survival are those in which we know that earlier detection or better treatment can improve prognosis.

'One of the biggest improvements was seen with malignant melanomas. This suggests that heightened awareness of skin cancer has encouraged people to contact their doctors early if they are concerned.' Similarly, awareness of breast cancer improved in the 1980s, before screening programmes.

Karol Sikora, clinical consultant to the fund, said the figures were encouraging, but greater government investment in cancer services was vital if Britain was to provide the same level of treatment obtainable in America and elsewhere in Europe.

In the US, figures based on diagnoses between 1986 and 1992 show a five-year survival rate of 84 per cent for female breast cancer, 61 per cent for bowel cancer, 87 per cent for skin cancer, and 14 per cent for lung cancer. But anomalies in the way the data are collected probably exaggerate the differences.

Professor Sikora said there was a lack of investment in cancer care. 'There are fewer specialists here than in America and most European countries.'

Cancer treatment in Britain varied from region to region and often patients did not push for the first-class treatment they deserved.

'People here are not as aggressive about health care as they are in America. The sort of delays people are having to put up with here wouldn't be tolerated in France or America.'

© *The Guardian*
June, 1998

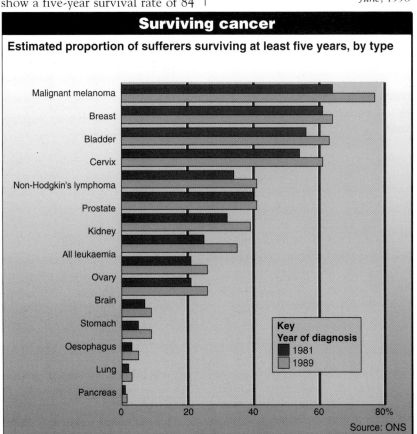

Surviving cancer

Estimated proportion of sufferers surviving at least five years, by type

Malignant melanoma, Breast, Bladder, Cervix, Non-Hodgkin's lymphoma, Prostate, Kidney, All leukaemia, Ovary, Brain, Stomach, Oesophagus, Lung, Pancreas

Key
Year of diagnosis
■ 1981
▨ 1989

0   20   40   60   80%

Source: ONS

The cancer lottery

Survival may depend on where you live

The lottery of breast cancer treatment is spelled out in NHS league tables published today.

They highlight for the first time the areas where women are most likely to die from the disease, which claims 13,000 lives each year.

Breast cancer charities said the information must be used to ensure all women have access to 'gold standard' treatment in future.

The figures reveal that women are far more likely to die of breast cancer in the Midlands. Nine of the 13 health authorities there have death rates above the national average.

The tables assign a national average figure of 100. Higher than that means an area has a death rate worse than average.

Solihull in the West Midlands has the worst record with a death rate of 119. Walsall comes second with 118. The Isle of Wight has the lowest at 81. All 11 health authorities in the Trent region have death rates above average – in most cases well above average. One, Barnsley, has the third highest death rate in England.

The Anglia and Oxford region, which includes nine health authorities, does better except for Northamptonshire, which scores 114.

The North Thames region – covering 14 health authorities, many in London – is generally well below the national average, as might be expected in an area which is home to many of Britain's finest hospitals. However, North Essex is an exception at 112, making it one of the worst areas in England.

The South Thames region also does well, with six authorities having fewer deaths than average, although Kingston and Richmond is an exception at 109.

In the North-West, death rates are at or below the national average in 12 of the 16 health authorities. Morecambe Bay has the lowest rate in the region at 82.

By Jenny Hope and Emily Wilson

Only two of the 13 authorities in the Northern and Yorkshire region have worse-than-average death rates.

Susan Osborne of the Cancer Research Campaign said it was important for women to be confident of getting good treatment wherever they live. She pointed out, however, that the number of women dying from breast cancer has fallen over the last five years, partly because of better treatment.

'Women are taking more control of their destiny,' she said. 'They are demanding a second opinion or to be referred to hospitals with specialist facilities if they feel the service isn't good enough.'

Data in the tables had to be interpreted cautiously, she said. Higher than average death rates did not always mean poor treatment but may mean higher incidence of the disease, CRC research had shown.

'It found all women in Glasgow received the same treatment regardless of their socioeconomic status but the disease was more advanced in women from poorer areas of the city,' she said. 'Women from ethnic minorities also tend to delay going to the doctor.'

Delyth Morgan, chief executive of the breast cancer charity Breakthrough, said: 'A modern health service has to be able to provide a minimum standard of quality for treatment regardless of where you live.'

Dr Evan Harris, Liberal Democrat NHS spokesman, said, however: 'The danger is that the publication of figures like this as league tables is more of a gimmick than a useful health education measure.'

Wife who got the bad news too late

Barbara Rae had a double celebration when doctors gave her the all-clear from cancer in September 1994 – on her 43rd birthday.

Yet seven months later, a biopsy revealed a malignant tumour the size of a large orange in her left breast.

The cancer had spread to her

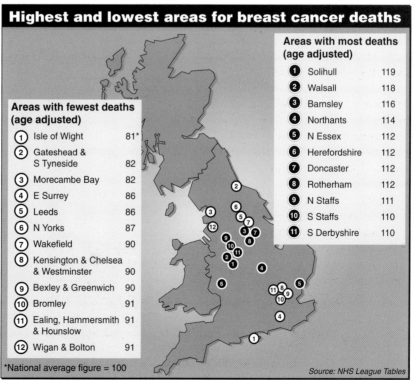

Highest and lowest areas for breast cancer deaths

Areas with most deaths (age adjusted)

1	Solihull	119
2	Walsall	118
3	Barnsley	116
4	Northants	114
5	N Essex	112
6	Herefordshire	112
7	Doncaster	112
8	Rotherham	112
9	N Staffs	111
10	S Staffs	110
11	S Derbyshire	110

Areas with fewest deaths (age adjusted)

1	Isle of Wight	81*
2	Gateshead & S Tyneside	82
3	Morecambe Bay	82
4	E Surrey	86
5	Leeds	86
6	N Yorks	87
7	Wakefield	90
8	Kensington & Chelsea & Westminster	90
9	Bexley & Greenwich	90
10	Bromley	91
11	Ealing, Hammersmith & Hounslow	91
12	Wigan & Bolton	91

*National average figure = 100

Source: NHS League Tables

bones. The philosophy lecturer was terminally ill. Misdiagnosis had cut her chances of survival from more than 50 per cent to 10 per cent.

A mammogram and clinical examination at Queen Alexandra Hospital in Cosham, Hampshire, that June had suggested Mrs Rae had a growth but further tests failed to find any problems and doctors put her on antibiotics for a 'mild breast infection'.

The symptoms continued and she was referred back to the hospital. In March 1995 she received the devastating news that she had terminal breast cancer.

It was so advanced that it was

too late for surgery. Mrs Rae, now 47, who has children aged nine and six, has had radiotherapy and

chemotherapy to slow the spread of the disease.

Portsmouth Hospitals NHS Trust, which runs the hospital, paid her £100,000 compensation just before the case was due to come to court.

Prince Charles yesterday called on men to help fight breast cancer. 'It is the biggest health concern to women but the reality is that fathers lose daughters, brothers lose sisters, sons lose mothers and husbands and partners lose much-loved ones,' said the Prince, new patron of the breast cancer research charity Breakthrough.

© The Daily Mail
December, 1998

Good screen guide

Where chances rise of breast cancer detection

By Jenny Hope, Medical Correspondent

Where a woman lives appears to be a big factor in whether she might have breast cancer and whether it will be detected.

The detection rate in the South-East corner of England is the highest in Britain and almost double that in Northern Ireland, according to NHS Breast Screening Programme figures.

Julietta Patnick, the programme's national coordinator, said it was well established that better-off women were more likely to be affected by breast cancer.

This, she suggested, could help explain why the detection rate among women having their first X-ray screening was 7.83 per 1,000 tested in the relatively wealthy extreme South East compared with 4.02 in Ulster.

Scientists are unable to agree why a rich region should have a high rate.

Whether a woman develops breast cancer could be affected by her lifestyle, diet and alcohol drinking. Better-off women could be more likely to attend screenings. Or the different detection rates could be explained partly by different screening practices.

More women than ever before were tested for breast cancer in the

12 months spanning 1996/97, according to the programme's latest figures. The total was 1.26 million, with three out of four accepting their invitation to have a check. More

cancer cases were detected – 7,141 compared with 6,664 in the previous 12 months.

A record number of these were found at an early stage when the disease is most curable – 3,156 of the cancers, an increase of 12 per cent, were smaller than 15mm. As a result, the screening programme appears to be on target to save 1,250 lives each

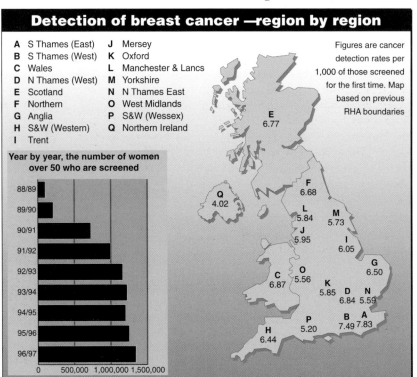

Detection of breast cancer —region by region

A	S Thames (East)	J	Mersey
B	S Thames (West)	K	Oxford
C	Wales	L	Manchester & Lancs
D	N Thames (West)	M	Yorkshire
E	Scotland	N	N Thames East
F	Northern	O	West Midlands
G	Anglia	P	S&W (Wessex)
H	S&W (Western)	Q	Northern Ireland
I	Trent		

Figures are cancer detection rates per 1,000 of those screened for the first time. Map based on previous RHA boundaries

E 6.77
Q 4.02
F 6.68
L 5.84
M 5.73
J 5.95
I 6.05
G 6.50
C 6.87
O 5.56
K 5.85
D 6.84
N 5.59
P 5.20
H 6.44
B 7.49
A 7.83

Year by year, the number of women over 50 who are screened

88/89
89/90
90/91
91/92
92/93
93/94
94/95
95/96
96/97

0   500,000   1,000,000 1,500,000

year. Breast cancer kills almost 14,000 women annually in England and Wales, one of the highest death rates in the world.

The £37 million-a-year breast screening programme offers X-ray checks every three years to women aged 50-64. Mrs Patnick was concerned at a slight fall in the number of women attending the later tests. They could be complacent or, having found the courage for the first screening, could not fact it again, she said.

About one woman in every 1,000 screened will develop breast cancer in the two years following an X-ray. One in four cancers found during the later checks may have been present at the previous X-ray but gone unnoticed.

Though two out of three breast cancers were diagnosed without the woman having to have surgery to check whether a lump was cancerous, 3,000 biopsies were carried out in which the lump turned out not to be cancer.

Mrs Patnick said: 'It is a balancing act between finding cancers earlier than before and not carrying out unnecessary biopsies.'

The number of women aged 65 and over screened also rose, from 57,000 to almost 67,000. They are not automatically invited for screening though they are at greater risk and the Government is being urged to include them in the programme.

© The Daily Mail
November, 1998

The essential guide to breast awareness

It is important that every woman should become aware – and remain aware – of her breasts throughout her lifetime. Breast size and shape vary considerably from woman to woman, and so do nipple size and shape. Breast awareness means knowing how your breasts look and feel normally so that you will be able to detect any change which might be unusual for you.

Most breast problems will prove to be benign (harmless). Although breast problems can sometimes be painful, they can usually be treated easily and rapidly. Breast problems should always be reported to your doctor.

It is really important to be breast aware because breast cancer is a possibility for all of us, including men. Each year, approximately 200 men get breast cancer, so men too should report any problems to their doctor.

Detecting a change early means that if cancer is then diagnosed, any treatment may have a better outcome. It is also worth remembering the good news. Nine out of ten breast problems are not caused by cancer.

Normal lifetime changes

A woman's breasts can go through many changes throughout her lifetime. They are affected by hormonal changes during her menstrual cycle, pregnancy, breast feeding, and the menopause (change of life).

The menstrual cycle

Each month, during a woman's reproductive years, her breasts prepare for pregnancy and breast feeding. Breasts often become enlarged and tender shortly before a period starts but return to their normal size once the period is over.

The menopause

Breast tissue changes after the menopause. It becomes less dense and firm, and more fatty, making the breasts feel softer. As we grow older, they may get smaller and become less firm.

All these changes are quite normal. However, if you feel or notice any unusual change in your breasts, you should see your GP at once to check whether you need further examination or treatment.

Checking for changes
When?

- Women should start being breast aware from the age of 18, and should continue their breast checks throughout their lives.
- It is best to try and get into a regular breast self-examination routine. Examine your breasts

THE WELL WOMAN CLINIC TODAY

once a month, preferably just after the end of your period. If you no longer have periods, or have irregular cycles, make a note to check your breasts on the same day each month.

How?
There are four easy steps to follow.

- First, stand in front of a mirror with your hands by your side, and look closely at your breasts. What you are looking for are any changes in their appearance.
- Now, with your hands on your hips, press down and tense your chest muscles. This will make any changes easier to see.
- Now raise your hands above your head and concentrate on the upper part of the breast that leads into the armpit.
- Finally, feel each breast in turn, using the opposite hand spread flat. Press gently, but firmly, in a circular motion with the pads of your fingers. Check your whole breast area starting deep in the armpit, moving over the top of the breast, then around and underneath it, finally circling around and over the nipple. Think of the procedure as a spiral moving inwards to the centre of your breast. The best way of doing this part of the check is to lie flat on your bed or with soapy hands while taking a shower or having a bath.

What am I checking for?
When you examine your breasts you are feeling for, or looking for, certain changes.

- A lump, or thickening, within the breast.
- A change in size. It may be that one breast has become larger; or one breast has become lower; or a nipple has become inverted or changed its position or shape.
- Any swellings under either armpit or around the collar bone (where the lymph nodes or glands are).
- Other symptoms to look for include a rash, or change in skin texture or colour; puckering or dimpling of the skin; discharge from one or both nipples; or constant pain in one part of your breast or in your armpit.

Be breast aware – and take action
If you notice any unusual changes, or if you simply want more information about being breast aware, contact your GP or practice nurse at the doctor's surgery.

Nine out of ten breast lumps are not a sign of breast cancer.

For more information and support, please telephone the Breast Cancer Care helpline on: 0500 245 345. Monday to Friday 10am-5pm.

Benign (non-cancerous) conditions
Mastalgia (breast pain and tenderness)
Pain is the most common breast problem affecting women. Breast pain can be cyclical or non-cyclical.

- Cyclical pain – is associated with your monthly period. Typically, breasts feel heavy, swollen and tender for several days before each period.
- Persistent or intermittent non-cyclical pain is often described as a 'burning' or 'drawing-in' sensation.

Continuing breast pain, whether cyclical or non-cyclical, should always be investigated. Your doctor may ask you to keep a 'pain chart' for a few months to help decide which type of breast pain you have.

Lumpy breasts
Women with naturally nodular (lumpy) breasts tend to find their breasts are especially sensitive around the time of their periods. Being breast aware will help you to recognise what is normal for you.

Other types of lumps appear unexpectedly. These include fibroadenomas and cysts.

Fibroadenoma
A fibroadenoma is a single lump of fibrous tissue which can be large, and usually feels firm but mobile. It may have to be removed surgically if it causes discomfort, is distorting the shape of the breast or becomes very large. This condition is usually found in women under 35 years of age.

Cysts
These are fluid-filled sacs which can feel either soft or firm and can sometimes be quite painful. There may be several cysts of varying sizes in one or both breasts.

Cystic breasts are common in women approaching the menopause. If the cysts are large enough, a hospital doctor can draw off the fluid using a syringe with a very fine needle. This is called 'aspiration'. If there is any cause for concern, the fluid will be sent to the laboratory for analysis.

Nipple disorders
Nipple discharge can be yellow, milky or blood-stained. It is usually the result of hormonal influences and may not need treatment. A discharge sometimes indicates an infection which can usually be treated by antibiotics.

Many women have flat or inverted nipples which are normal

for them. Whatever your normal appearance, you should always report an unusual change of any kind to your doctor.

Nipple soreness is most likely to be a form of eczema which is easy to treat. In rare cases, however, it may indicate a more serious condition, so, again always report any problem to your doctor.

What to do if you find a change

If you do notice a change, see your doctor as soon as possible. Don't worry that you may be making an unnecessary fuss. You know better than anyone how your breasts feel and look 'normally'.

Your doctor will examine your breasts and may then decide that you need to see a specialist for a more detailed examination. If so, an appointment will be made for you to attend a local breast clinic. Your doctor should have a copy of the *Macmillan Directory of Breast Cancer Services* which lists all such services in your area. If your doctor does not offer to send you to a breast clinic, and you are still concerned, or if the problem does not go away, you can ask to be referred to a specialist.

After examining your breasts, the specialist at the breast clinic may decide you need further tests. These may include a mammogram, ultrasound and fine needle aspiration.

Mammogram
A mammogram is a breast X-ray. Each breast is held firmly between two X-ray plates. Some women find this an uncomfortable procedure, but it only lasts a few seconds.

Breast ultrasound
This test is painless and is particularly useful for younger women (under 40) because their denser breast tissue makes it difficult to get a satisfactory image from a mammogram.

Ultrasound waves are sent to and from your breast by gently moving a special sensor over the breast. This forms pictures of your breast on a screen which can be 'read' by the specialist.

Fine needle aspiration
This is a quick and simple test, similar to a blood test. It is the same procedure that doctors use for cyst aspiration. The doctor draws off a few cells from a breast lump using a syringe with a very fine needle. The samples are then sent to the laboratory for analysis.

Getting your test results

At most breast clinics the results of these tests may take several days to come through. However, more and more 'one-stop breast clinics' are being set up. These clinics offer examination, testing and diagnosis all on the same day. If you would prefer to have a speedy diagnosis, ask your GP to refer you to a one-stop clinic if there is one near to where you live.

Screening for breast cancer

Every woman between the ages of 50 and 64 is entitled to be screened every three years as part of the National Breast Screening Programme. Your invitation for screening may come from your GP or you can ask to be referred yourself.

Screening for breast cancer in this age group has been proved to save lives, so do take up your invitation to attend a screening clinic. Screening is done by mammography.

Younger women are not yet eligible for the National Breast Screening Programme because at present there is little evidence that mammography in the under-50s provides a definite benefit. This may be because breast tissue in younger women is more dense and opaque, and this can make it more difficult to interpret an X-ray. However, this policy may change when current research is completed; this research is looking at mammography screening for women aged between 40 and 50.

A small proportion of breast cancers are genetic (around 5%). Younger women who think they may have a risk of genetic breast cancer can ask their doctor to refer them to a family history breast clinic. Just because a close relative has breast cancer, it does not mean there is genetic breast cancer in your family.

If you are 65 or over you are still at risk and entitled to breast screening every three years on request. All you need do is to telephone or write to your breast screening unit to make an appointment, or arrange this through your doctor if you prefer.

Breast screening units are usually found in hospitals or mobile units. You can find out where your local unit is by telephoning the free NHS Health Helpline on 0800 6655 44 (0800 2244 88 in Scotland).

@ Breast Cancer Care, 1998

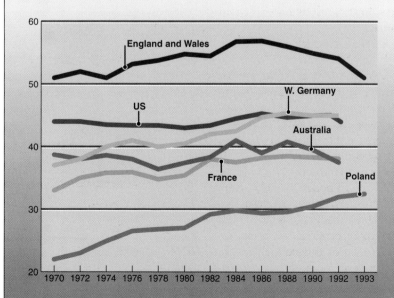

How we compare

International studies have shown that the age-standardised mortality rate per 100,000 for women with breast cancer in England and Wales is significantly higher than in the US, W. Germany, Australia, France and Poland. Age-standardised mortality rate per 100,000

The deadly delays

Thousands suffer on waiting list for cancer treatment

Thousands of cancer patients are dying or suffering weeks of unnecessary pain because of delays in receiving radiotherapy, it emerged yesterday.

More than a quarter are forced to wait 'unacceptable' times for the treatment, according to a national audit of cancer centres by the Royal College of Radiologists.

In some regions, desperately ill patients wait more than six weeks for life-saving treatment, although the maximum waiting time for radiotherapy has been set at four weeks.

Over the course of the year, up to 30,000 cancer patients are waiting too long for radiotherapy.

Dr Dan Ash, registrar at the Royal College of Radiologists, said: 'Delays in radiotherapy cause untold distress to patients, their families, their doctors and staff trying to treat them.

'I can't tell you how many people are dying because of delays, because the research has not been done, but cancer has to be treated as soon as possible. If it's not treated it keeps growing, sometimes very fast, and the risks increase.'

In the first study of its kind, the Royal College looked at waiting times at radiotherapy units around the country during one week in February.

Its researchers found that 28 per cent of patients treated that week – 556 cancer sufferers – had waited longer for their radiotherapy than the 'acceptable' times set out by the Joint Council for Clinical Oncology.

The North-West had the worst record, with 40 per cent of patients waiting longer than they should for the type of cancer they were suffering. The West Midlands had the best record, with only seven per cent experiencing delays. The wait was longest in the Northern and Yorkshire region, with 44 per cent of patients waiting more than six weeks for 'radical' life-saving radiotherapy.

By Emily Wilson, Medical Reporter

Experts blame the delays on the lack of radiotherapy machines. Another report published yesterday by the Royal College found that, while the number of patients needing radiotherapy has gone up by 18 per cent over the past five years, the number of machines has only been increased by three per cent.

'These things can cost up to £1 million to buy and set up but during their ten-year life span they will treat

Over the course of the year, up to 30,000 cancer patients are waiting too long for radiotherapy

up to 8,000 patients,' said Dr Ash. The 'unit cost' of treating a patient would therefore be as little as £125, he added.

Last night, Jean Mossman, chief executive of the charity CancerBACUP, said: 'The Government must honour its commitment to providing equal access to high quality care and to invest in radiotherapy services as a matter of urgency.'

The Government's pledge to put suspected cancer patients on a fast track from next April was condemned by doctors at the British Medical Association's annual conference in Cardiff on Monday.

They said the promise of an appointment with a specialist within two weeks was 'unreliable, inappropriate and impractical' and warned that other patients would suffer as a result. The association's GP leader, Dr John Chisolm, said: 'Cancer is a matter of urgency, but so are many other things.'

© *The Daily Mail*
July, 1998

Waiting for radiotherapy

Curative treatment for non-skin cancers. Maximum acceptable delay: 4 weeks.

	0-2 weeks	Over 4 weeks	Over 6 weeks
Northern & Yorkshire	20%	56%	44%
Trent	19%	30%	11%
Anglia & Oxford	24%	38%	30%
South-West	26%	34%	8%
West Midlands	45%	6%	0%
North-West	20%	24%	16%
North Thames	32%	31%	19%
South Thames	30%	24%	3%
Wales	33%	42%	25%
Scotland	18%	41%	26%
Norhern Ireland	13%	40%	33%
Total	**26%**	**32%**	**19%**

Source: Royal College of Radiologists

Sun protection and sunscreens

Protecting your skin from the sun is simple and doesn't need to be expensive

Remember to:

- head for the shade around midday
- avoid burning
- cover up with tightly woven clothing, a wide-brimmed hat and sunglasses.

Sunscreens also offer some protection but should only be used in combination with other methods. A sunscreen is any product applied to the skin to protect it from the sun. Almost any substance – make-up, lip balm, even dirt – will act as a sunscreen, although such means should not be relied on for protection!

Sunscreens may contain physical barriers, chemical absorbers or both. Physical barriers in sunscreens reflect the sun's harmful ultraviolet (UV) radiation away from the body. Chemical absorbers soak up UV radiation reducing the amount of UV that reaches the skin. A sunscreen's SPF is a measure of how much radiation it allows through.

What does SPF mean?

SPF stands for Sun Protection Factor and is a measure of how much a sunscreen protects your skin from burning in the sun. The higher the SPF, the greater the protection.

All sunscreens sold in this country carry an SPF rating on the front of the bottle. This rating may range from 2 to 30 or even higher.

A sunscreen's SPF is measured by timing how long skin covered with sunscreen takes to burn when compared with unprotected skin. So, if your unprotected skin would burn in 10 minutes in the midday sun, by using a sunscreen of SPF2, this would double the time spent before burning to 20 minutes. However, sunscreens should not be used to allow you to remain in the sun for longer – instead use them to give yourself greater protection.

How much sunscreen?

Most people apply sunscreens too thinly and generally end up with less

protection than the SPF on the bottle suggests.

When using a sunscreen, remember:

- apply it thickly and evenly over all exposed areas;
- those parts of the body which are not usually exposed to the sun will tend to burn more easily;
- pay particular attention to ears, neck, bald patches, hands and feet;
- re-apply regularly, especially after swimming.

Don't forget to protect your eyes

A good pair of sunglasses will help to protect your eyes from the sun. Look on the label for the British Standard BS2724: 1987. The most expensive sunglasses may not be the most protective!

SPFs and ultraviolet radiation

Two bands of ultraviolet or UV radiation reach the earth's surface – UVA and UVB. It is important for sunscreens to block out both UVA and UVB. The SPF number tells you how well a sunscreen blocks out UVB. It is much harder to measure its ability to protect against UVA. Different companies may use different ways of measuring this. The most common is a star system, which gives the ratio of UVA to UVB protection.

Which SPF?

Always choose a sunscreen with an SPF of 15 or above. It should also have 3 stars (***) or more. But do not rely on a sunscreen alone – you should still limit the length of time you spend in the sun.

Using after-sun creams

After-sun creams and lotions may help to soothe sunburnt or dry skin caused by the sun. But they can't help repair more serious skin damage.

- The above information is from the Health Education Authority campaign, Sun Know How.

© Health Education Authority (HEA), 1998

Childhood cancer

About childhood cancer

Childhood cancer is rare, about 1 in every 600 children develop cancer before the age of 15 – still relatively little is known about its causes.[1]

Childhood cancer is not a single disease – there are many different types. Compared with adult cancers they tend to have different histologies and occur in different sites of the body.[2] Common adult cancers such as lung, breast, colon, and stomach are extremely rare among children. On the other hand some types of cancer are almost exclusively found in children, especially embryonal tumours which arise from cells associated with the foetus, embryo, and developing body.

Leukaemia is the most common type of childhood cancer, representing about one-third of all cancers in under-15-year-olds. Leukaemia is a condition where too many underdeveloped white blood cells are found in the blood and bone marrow. Four-fifths of childhood leukaemias are acute lymphatic leukaemias (ALL), other types include acute myeloid leukaemia (AML) and chronic myeloid leukaemia (CML). Brain tumours are the most common solid tumours in childhood, and make up about a fifth of all children's cancers. There are many different types of brain tumours: medulloblastoma, astrocytoma and brainstem glioma are the most common.

Neuroblastoma (sympathetic nervous system), retinoblastoma (eye), Wilms' tumour (kidneys), and hepatobalstoma (liver) are most usually found in infants or young children. Other malignancies found in children and young adults include lymphomas (Hodgkin's and Non-Hodgkin's lymphoma), soft tissue sarcomas (including rhabdomyosarcoma), bone cancer (osteosarcoma and Ewing's sarcoma), plus a number of less common childhood cancers. Histiocytocis is rare; it is

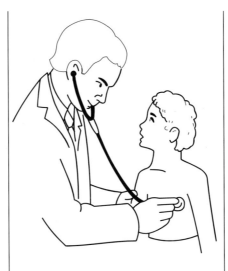

not a true cancer, but in many respects behaves like one.

The cause of most cancers remains unknown. A minority of cancers are known to be hereditary (inherited). For example some retinoblastomas, and Wilms' tumours are thought to be hereditary. In rare cases the family may have a history of cancers (Li-Fraumeni Syndrome)[4]. However most childhood cancers have no obvious hereditary cause.

Children with cancer are generally treated by specialists. Medical professionals who have expertise in diagnosing and treating children with cancer include paediatric oncologists, pathologists, haematologists, radiotherapists, surgeons, radiographers, and others; all of whom work closely together,

---

Leukaemia is the most common type of childhood cancer, representing about one-third of all cancers in under-15-year-olds

---

often in dedicated children's cancer centres. National and international children's cancer organisations have evolved in order to provide the best treatments, and are constantly engaged in research to further understand and develop better treatments for childhood cancer.

The overall cure rate for childhood cancer has drastically improved over the last two decades in association with clinical trials and the development of new treatments [5,6].

References and information sources

1 Stiller CA. Aetiology and epidemiology. In Plowman PN, Pinkerton CR, *Paediatric Oncology: Clinical practice and controversies.* Chapman and Hall Medical 1992.

2. Miller RW, Young JL, Novakovic PH. Childhood Cancer. *Cancer* 1994;75:395-405.

3 Stiller CA, Allen MB, Eatock EM. Childhood Cancer in Britain: The National Registry of Childhood Tumours and Incidence Rates 1978-1987. *European Journal of Cancer* 1995; 31A:2028-2034.

4. Birch JM. Li-Frameni Syndrome. *Eur. J. Cancer* 1994;30A:1935-41.

5. Lukens JN. Progress Resulting from Clinical Trials: Solid Tumours in Childhood Cancer. *Cancer* 1994;74:2710-8

6. Draper G, Kroll ME, Stiller C. Childhood Cancer. In: Trends in Cancer Incidence and Mortality. *Cancer Surveys* 1994;19,493-517.

• This guide is by Simon Cotterill, North of England Children's Cancer Research Unit, Department of Child Health, University of Newcastle upon Tyne, UK. This information can be found on their web site: http://www.ncl.ac.uk/child-health/guides/guide2c.htm

Right diet may help prevent cancer

The British approach to food is causing major health problems, according to new research. Sarah Boseley reports

Up to 80 per cent of all breast cancers and bowel cancers could be prevented if people improved their eating habits, according to scientists at Cambridge University.

John Cummings and colleagues at the Dunn Clinical Nutrition Centre believe that neither the public nor doctors take diet seriously enough. The British way of nourishment, with its emphasis on meat, processed food like sausages, and dearth of fruit and vegetables, is causing the nation major health problems, they say, and may be the reason why cancer rates in the UK are far higher than they are in other places, such as the Mediterranean.

Their study, published in the *British Medical Journal*, looks at the biological evidence which suggests that cancers can be caused by the food we eat. In each type of cancer, there are other risk factors, such as smoking, obesity, infections, sexual behaviour and exposure to sunlight, but 'food and drink has a part to play in many, if not all cancers, albeit to a variable extent'.

In general, their message is that red and processed meat and alcohol increase the risk of cancer, while fruit, vegetables and fibre have a protective effect. They say there is no evidence that vitamin supplements help prevent cancer and advise people that high doses can sometimes be harmful.

In March this year, a row broke out when the Government's Committee on the Medical Aspects of Food produced a report on diet and cancer. They were accused of making a U-turn in a desire not to damage the meat industry further when they recommended that anyone who eats more than 140 grammes (five ounces) of red meat a day – or 14 portions a week – should consider cutting down.

Average meat-eaters need not change their habits, they advised, even though the Health Secretary, Frank Dobson, had said six months earlier that they should. The World Cancer Research Fund at the same time said people should not eat more than 80 grammes (2.8 ounces) a day.

The Dunn scientists have kept their distance from arguments over the exact quantity that is safe, although they note that 15 per cent of consumers, mainly men, eat more meat than the Department of Health advises. But their research effectively strengthens the health message that changes in diet are needed.

'High consumption of meat, especially red meat and processed meat, is linked with higher risk of bowel, breast, prostate and pancreatic cancer,' they say. 'There is some evidence of an association with lung cancer, and of an association of barbecued meat and oesophageal cancer.'

We should be eating far more fruit and vegetables, they say. 'What is remarkable about the diet-cancer story is the consistency with which certain foods emerge as important in reducing risk across the range of cancers. Vegetables and fruit are almost invariably protective for the major cancers.

Cancer: the high-risk diets and lifestyles

Cancer type/site	High risk foods	Foods that lessen risk	Other risks	Health enhancing
Colorectal	Red meat, processed meat	Vegtables, non-starch polysaccharides (fibre)	Obesity	Physical activity
Breast	Alcohol, red meat, fried meat	Vegetables	Late menopause, late first pregnancy, obesity	Physical activity
Lung			Smoking, occupation	Physical activity
Stomach	Salt, pickled and preserved food	Fruit and vegetables, vitamin C		
Prostate		Vitamin E		
Cervix		Fruit and vegetables, vitamin C	Smoking	
Endometrium			Exposure to unopposed oestrogen, obesity	
Oesophagus	Alcohol	Fruit and vegetables	Smoking	
Pancreas			Smoking	
Bladder		Fruit and vegetables	Smoking, occupation	
Liver	Alcohol			

What to do
- Do not smoke
- Take regular exercise
- Do not be sexually promiscuous
- Avoid prolonged exposure to direct sunlight
- Avoid hepatitis B and C risks

Deaths from all cancers in England and Wales, 1996
Men: 72,464
Women: 66,995

What to eat and drink
- Eat plenty of fruit and vegetables (at least five portions a day)
- Avoid highly salted and mouldy foods
- Maintain ideal body weight (body mass index 20-25), avoid fatty foods
- Eat red meat and processed meat in moderation (no more than 140g a day)
- Avoid high doses of vitamin supplements
- Alcohol in moderation (a maximum of two units a day for women and three units a day for men)
- Eat plenty of cereal foods, mainly in an unprocessed form (as a source of non-starch polysaccharides)

'Consumption of these foods in Britain is less than half that in Mediterranean populations, where cancer rates are low. Average consumption of fruits and vegetables in Britain should at least double to five portions a day.' Consumption of fibre should increase from 12g a day to 18g a day.

Alcohol, they say, 'is a significant risk factor' for upper gastro-intestinal cancer, liver cancer and breast cancer. Intake should be restricted to no more than two units a day for women and three for men.

Dr Cummings said yesterday that the team wanted to get the message about diet and cancer through to doctors. 'We felt that in writing for this particular audience we could not afford to if and but too much,' he said. 'There is a feeling amongst medical people that this is not a serious way of preventing illness. Yet all the evidence points to diet being a major risk factor for cancer.'

The British do not take their diet seriously, he feels. 'I don't think people believe fundamentally that

'There is a feeling amongst medical people that this is not a serious way of preventing illness. Yet all the evidence points to diet being a major risk factor for cancer.'

diet is important to health here. It is a long-term thing. If you stop smoking you get respiratory improvements within months, but with diet, changes take 20 to 40 to 50 years.'

The poor British diet was a stark contrast with many other countries. 'Mediterranean countries take less interest in a healthy diet than we do, but they already eat a pretty healthy one.' Few people had changed their habits in the UK in spite of being told that fruit and vegetables are good for them. The study found different dietary risks for different cancers, although the overall conclusions on meat and vegetables hold for them

all. Fat in the diet has not been confirmed as a risk factor for breast cancer, but 'both meat and alcohol are associated with increased risk'.

The evidence is strongest in colorectal (bowel) cancer, they say. 'People who report eating greater amounts of "red" and processed meat are at higher risk of colorectal cancer. "Red" meat is taken to mean beef, pork and lamb in main dishes, and processed meat includes sausages, hamburgers, smoked cured and salted meat (including ham and bacon), and canned meat.'

The authors conclude that a better diet would protect not only against cancer but also other diseases, such as heart disease, hypertension and diabetes. 'Further, a plant-based food economy is much more sustainable than one based on livestock. Provided that other lifestyle factors are also taken into account, the diet for cancer prevention can, on the basis of current knowledge, form the basis for a rational public health policy.'

© The Guardian
December, 1998

New approaches to cancer

Through positive self-help

New approaches to cancer

New Approaches to Cancer is the national registered charity set up to promote the benefits of holistic and self-help methods of healing for cancer patients.

Our office acts as the nerve centre for a network of local self-help groups, holistic practitioners and clinics throughout the United Kingdom. We also have connections with other parts of the world, such as Europe, the United States of America, Mexico, Australia and so on. We operate a referral system and information service, directing people with cancer to their nearest sources of help.

What is the holistic approach?

Holistic therapy is the treatment of a person at all levels of their being – physical, mental, emotional and spiritual. The methods of treatment

are those which are considered best by the patient and their doctor through a process of informed consent.

Adopting the holistic approach does not mean using 'alternative' therapies alone, the emphasis is on treating the 'whole person' rather than just one particular part of the physical body. The holistic approach encourages people to examine their lifestyle in depth. Smoking, diet, imperfect nutrition and the pressures of everyday life (stress) can affect the individual's constitution, undermining good health and weakening the natural resistance to disease – including cancer.

Positive approach – positive attitudes

When cancer patients adopt the holistic approach, they start by taking

a positive, mental and emotional commonsense attitude to their disease. They learn to review their diet and discover the healing benefits of simple daily relaxation techniques. This is just a sample of the self-help methods we encourage people to use; not only those with cancer but also those who love and care for them.

We recognise that conventional medicine alone cannot overcome the sheer size of the cancer problem. Most families are affected by this disease, almost every adult can think of one or more of their loved ones who has suffered. Therefore our charity was established by people with a genuine concern, to give that extra help that can make a significant difference to the quality of life.

Attacking the cancer with external weapons such as surgery, radiation, drugs, etc. as offered by conventional medicine, is not enough. We encourage patients (and those who care for them) to learn from their local self-help groups how to complement existing medical techniques so that they have the best possible support system.

Our objectives

Our main objective is to show that cancer is survivable providing prompt action is taken by the person with the cancer, in conjunction with all the best facilities available. There needs to be a positive, definite commitment by the patient (and family) to adopt a proper plan of healing. As a first step this involves joining a local self-help group, and usually we can supply details of groups in most parts of the country.

Our further objective is to show that cancer is often preventable by a commonsense attitude. Our charity likes to feel that we have helped to sway public opinion to think green (and not before time!), to discourage smoking everywhere (a ridiculous habit of inhaling a multitude of toxins), to eat a healthy diet, to exercise consistently and correctly, and to ensure that all the pressures of life (stress) are counterbalanced by a positive approach that involves natural holistic therapies.

Progress

Since we began we have seen our referral directory grow to over 650 groups in the UK. We know there are many more groups being formed all the time in every city and town. We just need to know about them and the work they do so that we can expand our directory and share the knowledge in the common pool of available resources.

Major hospitals are beginning to acknowledge the value of this 'New Approach to Cancer' by opening up their wards to healers offering holistic therapies to those patients eager to receive this extra benefit. The famous Bristol Cancer Help Centre is well known for this valuable work.

'We all have a miracle of life given to us, the least we can do is honour that gift with caring love.'

How we can help you

Those seeking help from our charity can write to us sending (hopefully!) a large stamped, addressed envelope to the address on page 41 of this book.

The person needing help should give us brief details of the cancer, its location within the body and the date that the disease first became known (manifested). It is a help to know life details such as age, personal circumstances (i.e. married, children, etc.) and possible likely causes (smoking, bereavements, loss of job, stresses, and so on). There may be other facts that are important to know that need to be disclosed. It is an interesting point that the person who writes to us is often the spouse or loved one of those with the disease. This gives us an insight as to how cancer manages to encircle others as well as the patient on a mind level.

In return we provide details of the nearest local support groups and advice on useful reading material, based on our extensive library, written by experts and survivors from all over the world who support this New Approach to Cancer.

If we can we will draw on experience and suggest other sources of help. This will vary from person to person as to whether they wish to 'hear'. It will depend on the total preparedness and openness of those involved to embrace this extra help which can include, for example, the simple right to obtain a second medical opinion. We cannot however provide medical advice; that is for the chosen doctor to give after examination.

How you can help us

Our charity is run mainly by volunteers. Many of us have had personal cancer experiences which we can share with those in need. Naturally we look for more volunteers to expand our network but we do recognise that, for various reasons, some individuals and organisations cannot work with us and would prefer instead to make a financial contribution.

Our expenses are limited to telephone, printing and postage costs. We take great pride in being efficient and keeping our overheads down. We are cautious with expenditure and generous on the maximum help we can give in love. We have been on 'that road' and it is not pleasant to know such fear.

Every one of us in the country is directly or indirectly affected by cancer at some time or other. We all naturally wish to give or to help in various ways.

To get in touch

Our address is: New Approaches to Cancer, St Peter's Hospital, Guildford Road, Chertsey, Surrey, KT16 0PZ. Phone: 01932 879882. Fax: 01932 874349

Find us on the Internet at:

http://www.anac.org.uk

© New Approaches to Cancer

Cancer and complementary therapies

From the CancerBACUP booklet series

Introduction

This article has been written to explain the complementary therapies most often used for people with cancer. We hope that it will provide you with a balanced view of what is available so that, if you do want to try a complementary therapy, you will have a realistic idea of what it will involve and what it might do for you. Where the views of doctors and complementary practitioners are not the same, we will discuss and contrast these views so that you can make up your own mind.

Different philosophies of health have developed in different parts of the world, resulting in different attitudes towards illness and its treatment. Treatments used in this country are generally based on Western medicine, which uses a scientific model to prove the benefits of a particular treatment.

It is important for people affected by cancer to know the differences between the three types of treatment that they may receive or hear about:

1. Conventional therapies, which doctors use most of the time, consist of surgery, radiotherapy and chemotherapy. These treatments have usually been tested in clinical trials and through long experience with patients.
2. Complementary therapies are generally regarded as those treatments given alongside the conventional cancer treatments.
3. Alternative therapies are intended for use instead of conventional therapies.

Certain complementary therapies, such as counselling, are part of conventional treatment for some patients in many cancer centres, as doctors acknowledge the positive effects they can have on patients' well-being. Other complementary therapies such as relaxation and massage, while not part of conventional treatment, are accepted by doctors because they can help people feel better and cope better with their illness. These too are available in many cancer centres and also in settings outside hospitals.

Some treatments in the third category, alternative therapies, have caused a great divergence of view between doctors and alternative therapists. Most doctors believe that there is no evidence that such treatments can cure or reduce cancers. They also believe that these therapies may sometimes give people false hope and occasionally may even be harmful.

One reason why doctors have been reluctant to accept complementary and alternative therapies is that most of the treatments have never been scientifically studied or validated, apart from one study which showed a positive outcome of group psychotherapy on women with secondary breast cancer. Several scientific studies to evaluate these treatments are now in progress and will help to determine their real benefits. People with cancer can be very vulnerable, and there have been cases when such people have been misled by promises of a miracle cure. However, no reputable complementary or alternative therapist would claim to be able to cure or reduce cancer.

If you are thinking of going for treatment with either a complementary or alternative practitioner, it is important to make sure that they are properly qualified and will make a fair charge for the treatment. Always check that they are a member of a professional body, and always ask what the cost of the treatment will be in advance. It may be helpful to discuss your plans with your GP or cancer specialist beforehand.

Should I seek complementary or alternative therapy if I have been told I have cancer?

People should be encouraged to use conventional methods of cancer treatment, which have been scientifically proven. Complementary therapies may offer additional support and may help improve overall well-being. In the first instance you should consider discussing things with your GP or cancer specialist.

Sometimes people who seek complementary or alternative therapies do so because they are confused and lack information. They may feel there has been no time to discuss their questions and anxieties with their doctors. For many people, the more information and support that is available from the health professionals looking after them, as well as from organisations such as CancerBACUP, the less likely it is that they will seek help from a complementary or alternative practitioner. For others, complementary therapies are an important part of their being involved in helping themselves, in addition to what is offered at the hospital.

Although every effort has been made to ensure accuracy, Cancer-BACUP and its advisers cannot accept any liability in relation to this information. Readers are strongly advised to discuss the information with their doctor.

- The above information is reproduced from the CancerBACUP web site with their kind permission. This web site can be found at http://www.cancerbacup.org.uk Please see page 41 of this book for address details and information on their freephone helpline number.

© CancerBACUP

A risk worth taking?

An increasing number of people want to take part in drugs trials in the hope of finding a cure. Roger Dobson reports

Jayne Harrison was desperate to become part of a clinical trial. The 33-year-old dentist had been diagnosed as having breast cancer and was only too aware of the doubts about the effectiveness of existing drugs, particularly among women of her age.

'Being diagnosed at 33 as having cancer was pretty shitty, but I knew a lot of trials with new drug treatments were going on and, more than anything, I wanted to get involved, not just for myself, but in the hope that it could help others, too,' she says.

Jayne is one of a rapidly growing number of patients who choose to take part in clinical trials – the main way in which drugs and some other treatments are tested before becoming generally available. But although new drugs offer the patient the possibility of a more effective treatment, they can also turn out to be worse or no better than existing treatments and may also have side-effects. And for the doctors involved, trials can be a minefield of ethical problems and moral dilemmas.

Six days ago, doctors in the US blew the whistle on a study of the anti-breast cancer drug tamoxifen on the grounds that those women in the trial who had been taking it to prevent cancer were doing so well, it would be unacceptable to continue and deny the benefits to the women who had been taking a placebo. But critics of that decision say it means doctors and patients will not now get the long-term data they need from that study to establish the safety of a drug that would be taken by healthy women for many years.

The ending of the tamoxifen trial illustrates some of the dilemmas involved in the expanding area of clinical trials. It is estimated that there have now been around 400,000 trials since regulations on the safety of drugs were tightened in the aftermath of the thalidomide disaster. A single teaching hospital may now have up to 300 trials running at any one time and medical sites on the Internet are currently seeking volunteers for more than 5,500 trials, tackling a diverse range of diseases, from Alzheimer's and acne to vascular problems and vitamin deficiency.

Trails like these are the main examination that a new or improved drug has to undergo before it can be licensed for a specific condition. Before being trialled on patients, it will already have undergone tests on animals and small groups of healthy patients to identify any obvious side effects. In clinical trials, it is tested against a placebo or the best existing therapy and who gets what is usually determined by a random selection process.

But just who gets to participate in clinical trials remains something of a grey area, although the US National Cancer Institute recommends that they should be considered when there is no standard therapy available that works. Many patients, particularly those with advanced and life-threatening diseases, want to go on a clinical trial in the hope that they will be among those who get the new drug. Others do it for altruistic reasons, aware that while it may be too late for them it may help future sufferers. A few take part because they believe they will get better attention and observation, while others just want to get involved, to have a new hope.

Jayne enrolled because she felt she needed to do something after getting her diagnosis. 'I am a dentist but I was also doing a PhD in clinical trials, so I was very genned up on the pros and cons,' she says. 'I knew there was uncertainty about the treatment of breast cancer, particularly among pre-menstrual women, and I had decided that if it was malignant I wanted to be in a trial.

'At the time, I would have gone on any trial which did not affect my fertility, because I have no children and I didn't want my ovaries to get zapped or anything like that. In the end, I was put on trial involving tamoxifen as a treatment for breast cancer in the under-50s. It was a randomised trial which meant that the luck of the draw gave some people tamoxifen, others got nothing, and two other groups were given a combination of drugs or an injection. I got tamoxifen.

'I knew you had to accept what came along, whatever it was, but it was more important to me to be involved in a trial, any trial, than anything else. I felt that if some good came out of it, it was worth doing.'

Jayne believes that everyone should be aware of trials before they need them. 'I think that many know about clinical trials before they are ill, and I think people should be educated so they don't have to understand all the pros and cons at a time when they are also trying to come to terms with what is wrong with them.'

Hazel Thornton, founder and chairman of the Consumer Advisory Group for Clinical Trials, says

– YOU'RE NOT GOING TO RULE MY LIFE!

that giving people the right information is vitally important: 'People need to be given enough information and be presented with the case as it really is. It is vital that people make the right, informed decision.'

One of the dilemmas of the trials is that individuals who enrol often want a personal and immediate benefit while the trial itself will have wider goals. Professor Richard Lilford, adviser to the NHS on clinical trials, says: 'Desperate patients will want something to be done even if it is not yet proved, but society has to follow a policy which enables the correct evidence to be selected in the long term.

'The way to reconcile the imperative to help patients and the imperative to provide society with knowledge is to make a distinction between the two kinds of decision makers, the individual doctor who must do the best for the patient, and the state who must do the best for patients corporately.'

A second dilemma for doctors is an ethical test known as equipoise: 'A trial is ethical if there is genuine uncertainty as to what the best treatment is. If I embarked on a study when I had a good idea which was the best drug, that would not be equipoise. I could not expect a patient to accept randomisation if I had a good idea which was best,' says Professor Kent Woods, professor of therapeutics at Leicester University.

Clinical triallists are also keen to point out that there is always a referee involved checking on progress, even when both doctor and patients do not know which patient has the drug under test – a so-called double blind trial. 'Whenever a trial is going on, there will always be a group in the background who are not blind to the data and can see if one group is doing better or worse than another and can make a decision to stop the trial,' says Professor Woods.

But he adds: 'The decision to blow the whistle is a terribly difficult one. You are protecting the interests of the patients who agreed to take part, and at the same time there is the wider consideration about all the patients whose treatment is going to be influenced by the result of that trial.'

With the tamoxifen trial, the debate centres on whether it was the correct moment to stop that trial. Only time will tell if was the right decision.

Cancer vaccine may end chemotherapy

By Jeremy Laurance, Health Editor

A new era in cancer therapy could be opened later this year with the launch of a vaccine that tackles the disease in a different way and could spell the end of chemotherapy.

Melacine is the first cancer vaccine which has been developed as a treatment for advanced melanoma, the most aggressive form of skin cancer which claims 2,000 lives a year in the UK. The drug is expected to win approval from the US Food and Drugs Administration within the next six months after trials in patients showed 'promising' results.

A further five or six cancer vaccines are in the pipeline and are expected to be launched within the next two years. Some experts predict that they could mean the end of chemotherapy – treatment with large doses of toxic drugs whose side-effects can be worse than the disease symptoms – and usher in kinder therapies for people with cancer.

Cancer vaccines are so-called because they work by harnessing the body's immune system to fight the disease. They differ from conventional vaccines because they are given as a treatment rather than to prevent disease.

They are the first new class of drugs for cancer in a decade, since the taxanes were developed in the late eighties. These include the drugs Taxol, for advanced ovarian cancer, which is derived from the bark of the Pacific yew tree, and Taxotere, for advanced breast cancer.

Melanoma is the first cancer for which researchers have identified antigenic molecules – molecules, on the surface of the cancer cells, that are targeted by the immune system. Melacine, made by the US biotechnology company Ribi Immunochem, is one of a number of vaccines being developed for melanoma which primes the immune system to recognise the molecules and boosts its response to destroy cancer cells.

Professor Angus Dalgliesh, director of the Gordon Cancer Vaccine Laboratory at St George's Hospital, London, said: 'Cancer vaccines may well take over from chemotherapy. They will probably knock out chemotherapy in some adjuvant regimes [where it is given with other drugs].'

Most cancers had been developing for years in the body before they were diagnosed, during which time they turned off the immune response. The idea of cancer vaccines was to re-awaken the immune system.

He said: 'Where cancer vaccines are going to work is in cases where a solid tumour is removed and there is a high chance of the cancer coming back. They are the people who will get the vaccine to kick start the immune system. In most cases it will only delay the inevitable but if you can do that with a non-toxic treatment that will be a valuable advance.'

ADDITIONAL RESOURCES

You might like to contact the following organisations for further information. Due to the increasing cost of postage, many organisations cannot respond to enquiries unless they receive a stamped, addressed envelope.

Breakthrough Breast Cancer
6th-7th Floors
Kingsway House
103 Kingsway
London, WC2B 6QX
Tel: 0171 430 2086
Fax: 0171 831 3873
Funds research which aims to find methods of prevention and, ultimately, to eradicate breast cancer and establish the UK's first dedicated breast cancer research centre. Product a magazine three times a year called *Purple*.

Breast Cancer Care (BCC)
Kiln House
210 New King's Road
London, SW6 4NZ
Tel: 0171 384 2984
Fax: 0171 384 3387
E-mail:
breastcancercare@bccare.demon.co.uk
Breast Cancer Care is the national organisation offering information and support to those affected by breast cancer. Their services are free, confidential and accessible, and include a wide range of information resources, volunteer services and an aftercare service. Freephone helpline 0500 245345 open from Mon-Fri, 10am to 5pm.

CancerBACUP
3 Bath Place
Rivington Street
London, EC2A 3JR
Tel: 0171 696 9003
Fax: 0171 696 9002
CancerBACUP provides information and support to people with cancer, their families and friends. Specialist cancer nurses answer telephone calls and written enquiries concerning all aspects of cancer care. Also produces a wide range of booklets on the main types of cancer and their treatment, as well as the wider problems of coping with the cancer diagnosis. Information service 0171 613 2121. Freephone 0808 800 1234

Cancerlink
11-21 Northdown Street
London, N1 9BN
Tel: 0171 833 2818
Fax: 0171 833 4963
E-mail:
cancerlink@canlink.demon.co.uk
Cancerlink provides free confidential information on all aspects of cancer and emotional support to anyone with cancer, their families, friends and carers as well as health and other professionals.

Imperial Cancer Research Fund (ICRF)
61 Lincoln's Inn Fields
London, WC2A 3PX
Tel: 0171 242 0200
Fax: 0171 269 3262
E-mail: d.yabuca@icrf.icnet.uk
The ICRF is one of the world's leading cancer research organisations and is dedicated to the prevention, treatment and cure of all forms of cancer. A wide range of brochures and leaflets about cancer are available.

Leukaemia Research Fund (LRF)
43 Great Ormond Street
London, WC1N 3JJ
Tel: 0171 405 0101
Fax: 0171 405 3139
E-mail:info@leukaemia-research.org.uk
'We want to improve treatments, find cures and prevent all forms of leukaemia and the related cancers including Hodgkin's disease. We are committed to nationally organised research of the highest calibre, guided by strict impartial expert advice, and to international collaboration. We aim to co-ordinate fundraising throughout the UK towards these ends.'

Macmillan Cancer Relief
Anchor House
15-19 Britten Street
London, SW3 3TZ
Tel: 0171 351 7811
Fax: 0171 376 8098

Macmillan Cancer Relief is working towards the day when everyone will have equal and ready access to the best information, treatment and care for cancer.

Marie Curie Cancer Care
28 Belgrave Square
London, SW1X 8QG
Tel: 0171 235 3325
Fax: 0171 823 2380
Provides medical and nursing care for people with cancer through eleven Marie Curie Hospice centres throughout the UK and 5,000 Marie Curie nurses nationwide.

New Approaches to Cancer
St Peter's Hospital
Guildford Road
Chertsey, KT16 0PZ
Tel: 01932 879882
Fax: 01932 874349
Encourages people to look more deeply at the causes of their cancer by using complementary methods alongside orthodox techniques.

The Cancer Research Campaign (CRC)
10 Cambridge Terrace
London, NW1 4JL
Tel: 0171 224 1333
Fax: 0171 486 8317
Works to attack and defeat the disease of cancer in all its forms, and promotes its cure by research into its causes, distribution, symptoms, pathology and treatment, and to promote its cure.

Women's Nationwide Cancer Control Campaign (WNCCC)
Suna House
128-130 Curtain Road
London, EC2A 3AR
Tel: 0171 729 4688
Fax: 0171 613 0771
E-mail: wnccc@dial.pipex.com
Aims to promote the prevention and early detection of cancers affecting women by providing information to the public.

INDEX

age
  as a cause of cancer 2, 22
  and melanoma 12
AIDS (Acquired Immune Deficiency Syndrome), and
  cancer 2, 3
alcohol, as a risk factor in cancer 36

babies, and passive smoking 9
benign tumours 1, 30
body image, of people with cancer 25
bowel cancer, survival rates 26
brain tumours
  in childhood 34
  and mobile phones 25
breast cancer 3-6, 27-31
  and breast awareness 4, 26, 29-31
  deaths 27
  and diet 36
  drugs trials for 39
  family history of 4, 5
  genetic disposition 2
  and group psychotherapy 38
  and men 4, 5-6, 29
  misdiagnosis 27-8
  organisations 4
  regional variations in 27, 28
  risk factors 2
  screening 4, 5, 28-9, 31
  survival rates 26
breast lumps 3-4
breast pain 5, 30

carcinogens 2, 3
causes of cancer 1, 2-3, 22
cervical cancer 2, 3, 13-15
  causes 13-14
  deaths 13, 14
  prevention 14
  screening 13, 14, 15
  statistics 15
chemotherapy
  and prostrate cancer 21
  replaced by vaccines 40
  and testicular cancer 18-19
childhood cancer 34
children, and passive smoking 9, 10
clinical trials 39-40
close relationships and cancer 23-5
colon cancer 2
complementary therapies 36-8

deaths
  from breast cancer 27
  from cancer in the UK 20
  from cervical cancer 13, 14
depression, and people with cancer 24-5

developing countries, cancer epidemic in 7
diet 3, 5, 6, 35-6
drugs trials 39-40

electromagnetic fields, and male breast cancer 6
environmental causes of cancer 3, 5
European Community, numbers of new cancer cases 19

financial problems, and people with cancer 25
food/food additives
  and cancer prevention 35
  and carcinogens 3
friends, of people with cancer 24, 25

genes and cancer 1
  breast cancer 4, 5, 6
  genetic disposition 2, 22
  and testicular cancer 17, 18
global cancer cases 7

heart disease, and passive smoking 9
Hodgkin's disease 3
holistic therapy 36-7
hormone therapy, and prostrate cancer 20-1

immune systems 2-3, 22
  and cancer vaccines 40
Internet health sites 17, 39

leukaemia
  in childhood 34
  virus 3
liver cancer 3
lung cancer
  causes 2
  and passive smoking 9, 10
  survival rates 26
  and women 8
lymphomas 2

malignant melanomas 12, 26
malignant tumours 1
mammograms 4, 5, 28-9, 31
meat-eating, and cancer 35
melanoma 12, 26, 40
men
  and breast cancer 4, 5-6, 29
  and prostrate cancer 20-1
  and testicular cancer 16-19
metastases (secondary cancers) 1
mobile phones, and brain tumours 25

occupational risks, and male breast cancer 5, 6

pain killers, for breast pain 5
partners of people with cancer 4, 24, 25

primary cancer 1
prostrate cancer 20-1
public attitudes to sunbathing 11

radiotherapy
    delays in receiving 32
    and prostrate cancer 20, 21
'risky' behaviour, as a cause of cancer 22

secondary cancers 1
self-help, holistic therapy 36-7
skin cancer 2, 11, 12, 26
    and sun protection 33
smoking
    and cervical cancer 13-14, 15
    and lung cancer 2, 8
    passive 9-10
    in public places 9, 10
    and teenage girls 8
stress, and people with cancer 24
sun protection/sunscreens 11, 33
surviving cancer 26-8
    survival rates in Britain 26, 27

tamoxifen
    clinical trials of 39, 40
    for male breast cancer 6
teenage girls, and smoking 8
testicular cancer 16-19
    family history of 17, 19
    and infertility 16, 19
    risk factors 19
    self-examination 18
    symptoms 17-18
    treatment 16, 17, 18-19
tumours, benign and malignant 1

waiting lists for treatment 32
women
    and cervical cancer 13-15
    and lung cancer 8
    see also breast cancer

young men, and testicular cancer 16-17
young women
    and breast screening 31
    and cervical cancer 13, 14

* * * * *

CancerBACUP

(British Association of Cancer United Patients)
www.cancerbacup.org.uk
A huge site with loads of useful information. Issues covered include: specific cancers, coping with cancer, cancer treatments, talking about cancer and living with cancer.

Women's Nationwide Cancer Control Campaign (WNCCC)

www.dspace.dial.pipex.com/town/square/gm40/
A very useful site for information and factsheets on breast cancer including factsheets on: cancer screening in the UK, questions about breast problems and cervical cancer. Also offer information on other sources of help.

Macmillan Cancer Relief

www.macmillan.org.uk
This site provides useful extracts from their book, *The Cancer Guide*. This is a free 36-page booklet on cancer treatment and care. Also check their section, Help is There. This provides a list of cancer support and care organisations in the UK, with telephone numbers and addresses.

Imperial Cancer Research Fund

www.lif.icnet.uk
An excellent site. Visit Finding Cures, Saving Lives. These pages carry general and more specific information about cancer, weekly updated news, details of some of their research, contact information for BACUP and a glimpse into the future of cancer treatment and care.

Breakthrough Breast Cancer

www.breakthrough.org.uk
Breakthrough Breast Cancer is a charity committed to fighting breast cancer through research. Their site offers succinct but useful information.

University of Newcastle Upon Tyne

www.ncl.ac.uk/child-health/guides/guide2c.htm
Scroll to the bottom of the page and click on the world map. This will take you to a very useful guide to internet resources on childhood cancer.

The Cancer Research Campaign (CRC)

www.crc.org.uk
A very informative site. Take a look at the About Cancer section. This includes information on the facts, reducing risk, family cancer and further information.

CRC Institute for Cancer Studies

http://medweb.bham.ac.uk/cancerhelp
CancerHelp UK is a free information service about cancer and cancer care for the general public and health care professionals. It also offers information for young people and the general public. This site has excellent factsheets.

The Orchid Cancer Appeal

www.orchid-cancer.org.uk
A web site to promote awareness of prostate cancer and testicular cancer. This web site has been voted one of the best 100 medical web sites. It also has links to other relevant cancer web sites on the internet.

ACKNOWLEDGEMENTS

The publisher is grateful for permission to reproduce the following material.

While every care has been taken to trace and acknowledge copyright, the publisher tenders its apology for any accidental infringement or where copyright has proved untraceable. The publisher would be pleased to come to a suitable arrangement in any such case with the rightful owner.

Chapter One: Cancer Prevalence

What is cancer?, © CRC Institute for Cancer Studies at the University of Birmingham 1998, *What causes cancer?*, © CRC Institute for Cancer Studies at the University of Birmingham 1998, *Ten questions about breast problems*, © Women's Nationwide Cancer Control Campaign (WNCCC), *You don't have to be female to get breast cancer*, © The Independent, September 1998, *Which cancers kill most women*, © Cancer Research Campaign (CRC), *Global cancer cases 'to soar to 20 million'*, © Telegraph Group Limited, London 1998, *Women risk most deadly lung cancer*, © The Independent, December 1998, *The passive killer*, © The Daily Mail, March 1998, *Passive smoke row*, © The Daily Mail, March 1998, *The sun and your skin*, © Health Education Authority (HEA), 1998, *Attitudes to sunbathing*, © MORI (Market & Opinion Research International Ltd), *Skin cancer*, © Health Education Authority (HEA), 1998, *Protection against the sun*, © MORI (Market & Opinion Research International Ltd), *Cervical cancer research*, © Imperial Cancer Research Fund (ICRF), *Cervical cancer deaths fall by 40 per cent*, © Telegraph Group Limited, London 1998, *Cervical screening*, © Women's Nationwide Cancer Control Campaign (WNCCC), *The cancer young men ignore at their peril*, © Telegraph Group Limited, London 1998, *Testicular cancer*, © Imperial Cancer Research Fund (ICRF), *Numbers of new cancer cases in the EC, 1990*, © Scientific Year Book 1994-95, London Cancer Research Campaign, *Prostate cancer*, © Imperial Cancer Research Fund (ICRF), *Deaths from cancer*, © Imperial Cancer Research Fund (ICRF), *Why don't we all get cancer?*, © CRC Institute for Cancer Studies at the University of Birmingham 1998, *Close relationships and cancer*, © Cancerlink, *Mobile phones 'could be to blame for cancer surge'*, © The Daily Mail, January 1998,

Chapter Two: Treatment and Cures

More beat cancer, but UK trails other countries for cures, © The Guardian, June 1998, *Surviving cancer*, © Office for National Statistics (ONS), *The cancer lottery*, © The Daily Mail, December 1998, *Highest and lowest areas for breast cancer deaths*, © NHS League Tables, *Good screen guide*, © The Daily Mail, November 1998, *Detection of breast cancer – region by region*, © NHS Breast Screening Programme, *The essential guide to breast awareness*, © Breast Cancer Care, 1998, *The deadly delays*, © The Daily Mail, July 1998, *Waiting for radiotherapy*, © Royal College of Radiologists, *Sun protection and sunscreens*, © Health Education Authority (HEA), 1998, *Childhood cancer*, © Simon Cotterill, 1996-98, *Right diet may help prevent cancer*, © The Guardian, December 1998, *Cancer: the high-risk diets and lifestyles*, © The Guardian, December 1998, *New approaches to cancer*, © New Approaches to Cancer, *Cancer and complementary therapies*, © CancerBACUP, *A risk worth taking?*, © The Independent, April 1998, *Cancer vaccine may end chemotherapy*, © The Independent, July, 1998.

Photographs and illustrations:

Pages 1, 2, 4, 7, 8, 12, 13, 16, 21, 28, 39: Simon Kneebone, page 8: Katherine Fleming, pages 22, 24, 29, 30, 33, 37: Pumpkin House.

Craig Donnellan
Cambridge
April, 1999